WJEC
AS Biology

Gareth Rowlands

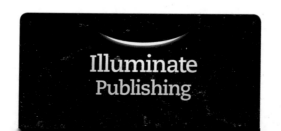

Illuminate Publishing

Published in 2012 by Illuminate Publishing Ltd, P.O Box 1160,
Cheltenham, Gloucestershire GL50 9RW

Orders: Please visit www.illuminatepublishing.com
or email sales@illuminatepublishing.com

British Library Cataloguing in Publication Data

A catalogue record for this book is available from the British Library

ISBN 978-1-908682-06-2

Printed by Wyndeham Grange

The publisher's policy is to use papers that are natural, renewable and recyclable products
made from wood grown in sustainable forests. The logging and manufacturing processes
are expected to conform to the environmental regulations of the country of origin.

Every effort has been made to contact copyright holders of material produced in this book.
If notified, the publisher will be pleased to rectify any errors or omissions at the earliest
opportunity.

This material has been endorsed by WJEC and offers high quality support for the delivery
of WJEC qualifications. While this material has been through a WJEC quality assurance
process, all responsibility for the content remains with the publisher.

Editor: Geoff Tuttle
Design and layout: Nigel Harriss

Cover image: © Cathy Keifer/Shutterstock

Image Credits:
Science Photo Library: p26 © Dr Jeremy Burgess; p27 © Don W. Fawcett; p28 © Medimage
(top), © Biology Media (bottom); p30 © Dr. George Chapman, Visuals Unlimited; p31 © Steve
Gschmeissner; p60 © Power And Syred; p93 © Power And Syred (top), Dr Jeremy Burgess
(bottom ×2); p97 © Dr Keith Wheeler; p110 © Dr Keith Wheeler (left), © Steve Gschmeissner
(right); p116 © Dr Keith Wheeler; p117 © Dr Keith Wheeler (Left), Biophoto Associates (Right);
p123 © Dr Keith Wheeler.

Shutterstock: p9 © Leonid Andronov; p14 © Gorilla; p18 © rob3000; p19 © Lorelyn
Medina; p20 © Sue Robinson (left), © Kenneth Sponsler (right); p25 © Jubal Harshaw; p31
© leonello calvetti; p35 © Dimarion; p45 © Leonid Andronov; p58 © Sebastian Kaulitzki; p60
© RN3dARTS; p61 © Dimarion; p68 © Dimarion (×5); p70 © Marcio Jose Bastos Silva; p74
© sgame; p75 © alxhar (left), © Judy Kennamer (right); p76 © Fotografiche; p77 unknown;
p78 © michael sheehan (centre), © Eric Isselée (right); p78 © Schalke fotografie | Melissa
Schalke (left); p83 © OceanImpressions; p88 © iliuta goean (left), © arnaud weisser (centre),
© Christopher Ewing (right); p89 © Jubal Harshaw; p91 © Jubal Harshaw; p94 © Jubal
Harshaw; p98 © ggw1962; p104 © Jubal Harshaw; p109 © Max Topchii; p124 © Frank F.
Haub; p125 © oksix (top), © alxhar (bottom); p128 © CLChang (left), © Alex_187 (right); p130
© mrfiza.

Acknowledgements
I am very grateful to the team at Illuminate Publishing for their professionalism, support and
guidance throughout this project. It has been a pleasure to work so closely with them.

The author and publisher wish to thank Dr John Ford for his thorough review of the book and
expert insights and observations.

Contents

How to use this book

The contents of the book closely match the specification for WJEC AS Level Biology and provide you with information and plenty of practice examination questions in order to prepare successfully for the BY1 and BY2 examinations.

This book covers all three of the Assessment Objectives required for your WJEC AS level Biology course. The main text covers AO1 Knowledge and Understanding, which consists of the main factual content of the specification and AO2 Application of Knowledge and Understanding. The other Assessment Objective, AO3 How Science Works, which covers around 5% of the assessment weighting of the specification, is covered in the form of a margin feature 'How Science Works'. You will not be asked to recall the information given under this heading for the purpose of the examination.

The book content is clearly divided into two Assessment Units, BY1 and BY2.

- BY1 covers Basic Biochemistry and Cell Structure.
- BY2 covers Biodiversity and Physiology of Body Systems.

At the start of each unit there is an overview page. Each unit is divided into a number of topics. Topic openers give a summary of the content to be covered together with a list of learning objectives.

At the end of the book there are answers to the Exam practice and Knowledge check questions, a glossary of key terms used in the WJEC specification and a detailed index to help you navigate through the book.

The text is supplemented with a number of features. ➜

YOU SHOULD KNOW ›››

››› The learning objectives provided are more specific to the sub-topic being studied than the more general learning objectives listed at the start of the topic.

Key Terms

Although there are terms that you need to define and understand included in the body of the text, where terms are not explained within the same topic these are highlighted in bold type within the text and are highlighted in blue as margin features. Terms can also be looked up in the glossary section which appears at the back of the book. The use of key terms is an important feature since examination papers contain a number of terms that need to be defined.

Knowledge check

These are short questions to check your understanding of the subject, allowing you to apply the knowledge that you have acquired. These questions are of two types: Filling in blanks in a passage, or matching terms with phrases specific to the topic under study. Answers are supplied at the back of the book.

How Science Works

This feature helps you understand something about science itself, how scientific knowledge has been obtained, how reliable it therefore is and what its limitations are. It may also help you to have a deeper awareness of how science is used to improve our quality of life. You will not be examined on the information provided by this feature.

▼ Study point

As you progress through your studies, advice is provided to help you understand and use the knowledge content. This may provide some extra information not included in the main text or simply point out that the information is relevant but may not be tested in the examination.

Examiner tip

The examiner may provide general or specific advice to help you with your studies and to prepare you for the exam.

Link

Links are highlighted in the margin near the relevant text. They are accompanied by a reference to any areas where sections relate to one another. It may be suggested that you recap a topic before beginning to study the current topic.

How Science Works

When science is encountered in everyday life, it is important not only to understand some of the fundamental scientific explanations of the behaviour of the natural world, but also to know something about science itself, how scientific knowledge has been obtained, how reliable it therefore is, and what its limitations are. It is also important to appreciate the impact that scientific knowledge has on society as a whole. In other words, you need to question what is going on in the science that impacts on your life.

In order to do this you should appreciate the following:

✓ Data from observations and measurements are of central importance.

✓ A good explanation may allow us to predict what will happen in other situations, enabling us to perhaps control and influence events.

✓ There may be a correlation between a factor and an outcome.

✓ Devising and testing a scientific explanation is not a simple and straightforward process. We can never be completely sure of the data. An observation may be incorrect because of the limitations of either the measuring equipment or the person using it.

✓ Thinking up an explanation is a creative step. It is quite possible for different people to arrive at different explanations for the same data.

✓ The scientific community has established procedures for testing and checking the findings and conclusions of individual scientists, and arriving at an agreed view. Scientists report their findings at conferences and in special publications.

✓ The application of scientific knowledge, in new technologies, materials and devices, greatly enhances our lives, but can also have unintended and undesirable side-effects.

The application of science may have social, economic and political implications, and perhaps also ethical ones.

'How Science Works' is developed in this book through relevant topics and is highlighted with the margin feature. These features will help you develop the relevant skills necessary for examination purposes and also give you an idea of how scientists work. This will enable you to have a deeper awareness of how science is used to improve our quality of life.

BY1

Use theories, models and ideas to develop scientific explanations.
→ Models of enzyme action: page 48

Data from observations and measurements are of central importance.
→ Testing for reducing sugar: page 11

An observation may be incorrect because of the limitations of either the measuring equipment or the person using it.
→ Observations from light and electron microscopy: page 36

Proposing a theory may account for the data.
→ Structure of DNA as proposed by Watson and Crick: page 58

BY2

The need to use a variety of evidence from different sources, in making valid scientific conclusions.
→ The theory of human evolution: page 80

Devising and testing a scientific explanation is not a simple and straightforward process.
→ The mechanism of translocation: page 118

Overview: BY1
Basic Biochemistry and Cell Structure

Biological molecules p9

Chemical properties of carbohydrates, fats and proteins related to chemical structure.

- Carbohydrates: a source of energy; polymers add strength and support.
- Fats: energy stores, insulation and protection, and component of cell membrane.
- Proteins: enzymes, hormones, antibodies, transport and structural.
- Water is an important solvent and is involved in biochemical reactions.
- Inorganic ions have important roles in biological molecules.

Enzymes p45

- Globular proteins.
- Lower activation energy.
- Combine with a substrate to form an enzyme–substrate complex.
- Properties related to tertiary structure.
- Affected by factors such as temperature, pH, and the concentration of the reactants.
- Inhibited by competitive and non-competitive inhibitors.
- Widely used in industry in immobilised form.

Cell structure and organisation p25

- Prokaryotes: simple organisms such as bacteria with no membrane-bound organelles.
- Eukaryotes: plants, animals, fungi and protoctists with membrane-bound organelles.
- In multicellular organisms cells become specialised for different functions.
- Cells are aggregated into tissues, tissues are organised into organs.

Nucleic acids and cell division p57

- Nucleic acids are composed of a phosphate group, a pentose sugar and an organic base.
- DNA and RNA are nucleic acids.
- DNA contains a deoxyribose sugar, whereas RNA has a ribose sugar.
- DNA is a double helix with base pairs bonded together; RNA is single stranded.
- The sequence of bases in DNA is called the genetic code.
- DNA replicates during cell division.

There are two forms of cell division:

- Mitosis:
  - Asexual reproduction and growth and repair of cells.
  - Daughter cells genetically identical to the parent.
  - One cycle of division results in the formation of two daughter cells.
  - Stages are interphase, prophase, metaphase, anaphase and telophase.
- Meiosis:
  - Occurs in the production of gametes.
  - Daughter cells genetically different.
  - One cycle involves two divisions and results in the formation of four haploid cells.

Cell membranes and transport p35

- Consists of phospholipids and proteins.
- Fluid mosaic model.
- Transport of materials by diffusion, facilitated diffusion, active transport, osmosis and bulk transport.

BY1 Biological molecules

The study of the structure and functioning of biological molecules is known as molecular biology. Molecular biology is closely linked with biochemistry, which is a study of the chemical reactions of biological molecules. Certain molecules have particular functions in living organisms. These functions depend on the properties that a molecule possesses. A molecule gets its properties from its structure.

By the end of this topic you should be able to:

- Understand the biological importance of carbohydrates, lipids and proteins.
- Describe the basic structure, properties and functions of carbohydrate: monosaccharides, disaccharides and polysaccharides.
- Describe how α and β isomerism in glucose results in storage and structural carbohydrates as illustrated by starch, cellulose and chitin.
- Describe the basic structure of triglycerides and phospholipids and relate these structures to their functions.
- Describe the implications of saturated and unsaturated fat on human health.
- Describe the primary, secondary, tertiary and quaternary structure of proteins.
- Describe the importance of the different types of bonds in maintaining the three-dimensional structure of a protein.
- Use given structural formulae of carbohydrate, lipids and proteins to show how bonds are formed and broken by condensation and hydrolysis, including peptide, glycosidic and ester bonds.
- Describe how the structure of carbohydrates, lipids and proteins is related to their functions.
- Describe the role of water in maintaining life on earth.
- Describe the roles of the inorganic ions: magnesium, iron, calcium and phosphate.

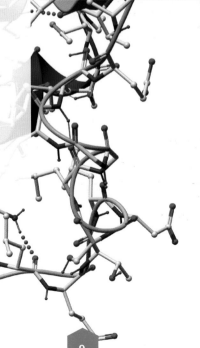

Key Terms

Isomers = compounds that have the same chemical formula but which differ in the arrangement of the atoms.

Polymers = long chains of repeating monomer units.

▼ Study point

Organic molecules always contain carbon.

Organic chemistry is the study of the chemistry of the element carbon and its compounds, whereas the chemistry of all other elements and their compounds is called inorganic chemistry.

Examiner tip

Many organic molecules, including carbohydrates, are made up of a chain of individual molecules, each of which is given the general name, monomer.

Carbohydrates

Carbohydrates are organic compounds containing the elements carbon, hydrogen and oxygen. In carbohydrates the basic monomer unit is called a monosaccharide. Two monosaccharides combine to form a disaccharide. Many monosaccharide molecules combine to form a polysaccharide.

Monosaccharides

Monosaccharides are relatively small organic molecules and provide the building blocks for the larger carbohydrates. Monosaccharides have the general formula $(CH_2O)_n$ and their name is determined by the number of carbon atoms in the molecule (n). A triose sugar has three carbon atoms; a pentose sugar has five carbon atoms. Glucose is a hexose sugar.

All hexose sugars share the formula $C_6H_{12}O_6$ but they differ in their molecular structure. Monosaccharides usually exist as ring structures when dissolved in water. Glucose exists as two **isomers**, the α form and the β form. These different forms result in considerable biological differences when they form **polymers** such as starch and cellulose.

It is usual to show the arrangement of the atoms using a diagram known as a structural formula:

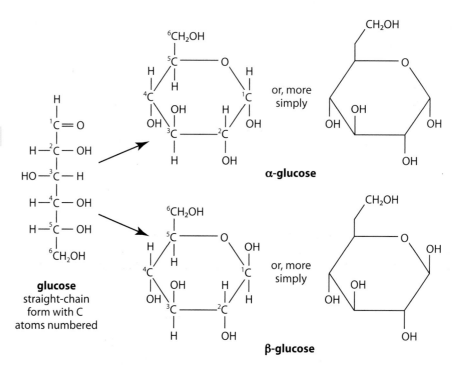

▲ Structural formulae for the straight chain and ring forms of glucose

Monosaccharides have two main functions:

- They are used as a source of energy in respiration. Carbon–hydrogen bonds are broken to release energy, which is transferred to make adenosine triphosphate (ATP) from adenosine diphosphate (ADP).

- They act as building blocks for larger molecules. For example, glucose is used to make the polysaccharides, starch, glycogen and cellulose.

Disaccharides

Disaccharides consist of two monosaccharide units linked together with the formation of a glycosidic bond *and the elimination of water*. This is called a condensation reaction. Disaccharides are formed by the combination of two monosaccharides.

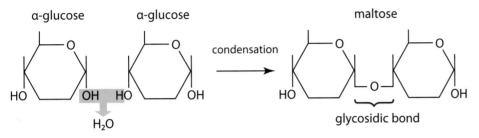

▲ *Formation of a glycosidic bond when two glucose molecules combine to form maltose*

Disaccharides can also be formed by the joining together of two different monosaccharides:

- Glucose and fructose join to form sucrose.
- Glucose and galactose join to form lactose.

Disaccharides are used for storage and transport. For example, carbohydrate is transported in the sieve tubes of phloem in the form of sucrose.

Testing for the presence of sugars

A Benedict's reagent is used to test for the presence of glucose in a solution. The test is carried out as follows.

Add an equal volume of Benedict's reagent (blue) to the solution being tested and heat in a boiling water bath. If a reducing sugar such as glucose is present, the solution will gradually turn through green, yellow and orange and finally a brick red precipitate forms.

Some disaccharides, such as sucrose, are non-reducing sugars and a negative test will be achieved. Sucrose can only be detected if it is first broken down to its constituent monosaccharides by heating with hydrochloric acid. Benedict's reagent needs alkaline conditions to work, so the solution is neutralised by adding alkali slowly until any fizzing stops. Add Benedict's reagent and heat as before. If the solution now turns red then a non-reducing sugar is present.

The Benedict's test is a qualitative, or at best, a semi-quantitative test. The diagram shows the relationship between the concentration of reducing sugar and the colour of the solution and precipitate formed. It is possible therefore to estimate the approximate level of reducing sugar in a sample.

▼ *Results of Benedict's test*

Test results

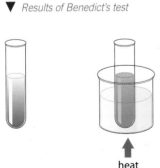

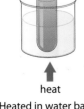

negative   very low   low   medium   high

heat

Colour depends on concentration of reducing sugar present in sample.

Equal volume of Benedict's reagent added to food sample dissolved in water.

Heated in water bath. If reducing sugar present solution turns orange-brown.

Examiner tip

The reverse of condensation is the addition of water and this is known as hydrolysis.

▼ **Study point**

As with most chemical reactions taking place in the cell, hydrolysis and condensation reactions are controlled by enzymes.

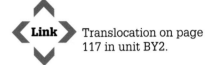

Link Translocation on page 117 in unit BY2.

How Science Works

Qualitative data consist of observations made without using measurements.

Quantitative data are made more precise by measurement.

Link Biosensors on page 53.

Examiner tip

You should refer to the position of atoms attached to the carbons by their number in the hexose ring. '1,4 linked' means that the glucose molecules are linked between carbon atoms 1 and 4 of successive glucose units, e.g. in the glycosidic bond in the diagram above.

Using a biosensor, a more accurate measurement may be obtained. Giving an actual value to the concentration of sugar present is much more valuable. This is described as a quantitative measurement.

Polysaccharides

Polysaccharides are large, complex molecules called polymers. They are formed from very large numbers of monosaccharide units linked together by glycosidic bonds.

Starch

Since glucose is the main source of energy in cells, it needs to be stored in an appropriate form. Glucose dissolves and would increase the concentration of the cell contents, and would draw water towards it by osmosis. This problem is avoided by converting it into a storage product, polysaccharide, which is insoluble. It is also a compact molecule and can be stored in a small space. Starch is found in plant cells in the form of starch grains. These are found in seeds and storage organs such as potato tubers.

Starch is made up of many α glucose molecules held together, and consists of two polymers, amylose and amylopectin. Amylose is linear (unbranched) and coils into a helix, whereas amylopectin is branched and fits inside the amylose.

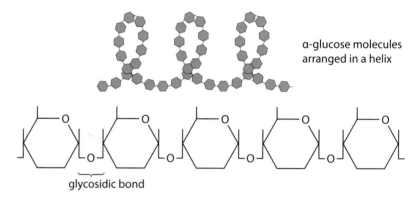

α-glucose molecules arranged in a helix

glycosidic bond

▲ *Structure of a molecule of starch*

The 1-4 linkages cause the chain to turn and coil. The main storage product in animals is called glycogen, sometimes called animal starch and is very similar to amylopectin, differing only in that glycogen molecules are more branched than the amylopectin molecules.

Both starch and glycogen are readily hydrolysed to α glucose which is soluble and can then be transported to areas where energy is needed.

Testing for the presence of starch

Add orange-brown iodine solution. A blue-black colour is produced if it comes in contact with starch.

Cellulose

Cellulose is a structural polysaccharide and is the most abundant organic molecule on Earth due to its presence in plant cell walls. Cellulose consists of many long parallel chains of β glucose molecules cross-linked to each other by hydrogen bonds. Being made up of β glucose units, the chain has adjacent glucose molecules rotated by 180°. This allows hydrogen bonds to be formed between the hydroxyl groups of adjacent parallel chains and helps to give cellulose its structural stability.

Between 60 and 70 cellulose molecules become tightly cross-linked to form bundles called microfibrils. These microfibrils are in turn held together in bundles called fibres. A cell wall has several layers of fibres running in different directions to increase the strength. Despite their strength, cellulose fibres are freely permeable, allowing water and solutes to penetrate through to the cell membrane.

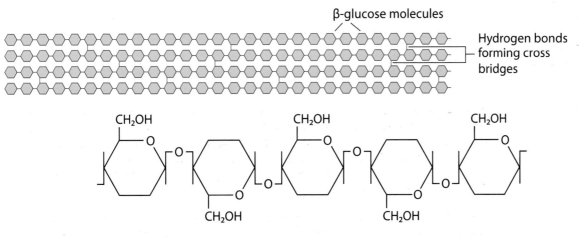

▲ *Structure of a molecule of cellulose*

Chitin

Chitin is a polysaccharide found in insects. It is similar to cellulose but has amino acids added to form a mucopolysaccharide. It is strong, waterproof and lightweight and forms the exoskeleton of insects.

▲ *Structure of a molecule of chitin*

Lipids

Like carbohydrates, lipids also contain carbon, hydrogen and oxygen but in proportion to the carbon and hydrogen they contain less oxygen. They are non-polar compounds and so are insoluble in water.

Triglycerides are formed by the combination of one glycerol molecule and three molecules of fatty acids. A triglyceride consists of one molecule of glycerol and three fatty acid molecules. The glycerol molecule in a lipid is always the same but the fatty acid component varies. The fatty acids join to glycerol by a condensation reaction whereby three molecules of water are removed and an oxygen bond, known as an ester bond, is formed between the glycerol and fatty acid.

$$\text{glycerol} \quad + \quad \text{3 fatty acids} \longrightarrow \text{triglyceride} \quad + 3H_2O$$

▲ *Formation of triglyceride*

> ▼ **Study point**
>
> Fatty acids are organic molecules which all have a –COOH group attached to a hydrocarbon tail. Glycerol is a type of alcohol.

The glycerol molecule is always the same but there are many different fatty acids that might react with glycerol.

Properties of lipids

The differences in the properties of different fats and oils come from variations in the fatty acids. If the hydrocarbon chain has no carbon–carbon double bonds then the fatty acid is described as saturated because all the carbon atoms are linked to the maximum possible number of hydrogen atoms. That is, they are saturated with hydrogen atoms. If there are double bonds present then the fatty acid is described as non-saturated. This is because the fatty acids have fewer hydrogen atoms than they might.

A high intake of fat, notably saturated fats, is a contributory factor in heart disease. Animal lipids are often saturated, whereas plant lipids are often unsaturated and occur as oils, such as olive oil and sunflower oil.

An important chemical property of lipids is that they are insoluble in water but dissolve in organic solvents such as acetone and alcohols.

▲ *Unhealthy and healthy diet*

▼ *Saturated and unsaturated fats*

saturated fatty acids

unsaturated fatty acids

Roles of lipids

Lipids play a major role in the structure of plasma membranes. Other roles of lipids include:

- Lipids make excellent energy reserves in both plants and animals. This is because they contain more carbon–hydrogen bonds than carbohydrates. One gram of fat, when oxidised, yields approximately twice as much energy as the same mass of carbohydrate.

- When stored under the skin it acts as an insulator against heat loss.

- Protection – fat is often stored around delicate internal organs such as kidneys.

- Triglycerides also produce a lot of metabolic water when oxidised. This is important in desert animals such as the kangaroo rat, which never drinks water and survives on metabolic water from its fat intake.

- Waterproofing – fats are insoluble in water and are important in land organisms such as insects where the waxy cuticle cuts down water loss. Leaves also have a waxy cuticle to reduce transpiration.

Phospholipids

Phospholipids are a special type of lipid. Each molecule has the unusual property of having one end which is soluble in water. This is because one of the fatty acid groups is replaced by a phosphate group which is **polar** and can therefore dissolve in water.

Phospholipids are important in the formation and functioning of plasma membranes in cells.

The lipid part is non-polar and insoluble in water (hydrophobic).

The phosphate group is polar and dissolves in water (hydrophilic).

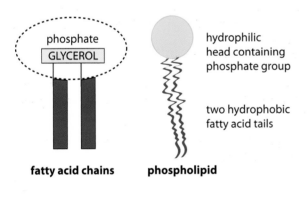

▲ *Structure of a phospholipid*

fatty acid chains   phospholipid

hydrophilic head containing phosphate group

two hydrophobic fatty acid tails

Key Term

Polar = molecules that have two ends or poles that interact differently to water and fat.

A hydrophilic head is attracted to water but not fat, whereas a hydrophobic tail mixes readily with fat but is repelled by water.

Examiner tip

Phospholipids allow lipid-soluble substances to enter and leave a cell and prevent water-soluble substances entering and leaving the cell.

Link The biological significance of the structure of phospholipids will become apparent when membranes are studied on page 36.

Knowledge check

Identify the missing word or words.

When triglycerides are hydrolysed they form fatty acids and ..... A fatty acid with more than one carbon-carbon double bond is said to be ..... Phospholipids are a special type of lipid where one of the fatty acids groups is replaced by a .... group. Phospholipids are an important component of cell .....

Proteins

YOU SHOULD KNOW ›››

››› the formation of a peptide bond

››› amino acids are linked together to form a polypeptide

››› the four levels of protein structure and the bonds involved

››› examples of secondary, tertiary and quaternary proteins

››› examples of fibrous and globular proteins and their functions

››› the Biuret test for protein

- Proteins differ from carbohydrates and lipids in that in addition to carbon, hydrogen and oxygen, they always contain nitrogen. Many proteins also contain sulphur and sometimes phosphorous.

- Proteins are large compounds built up of sub-units called amino acids. About 20 different amino acids are used to make up proteins. There are thousands of different proteins and their shape is determined by the specific sequence of amino acids in the chain.

- All amino acids have the same basic structure in that each possesses an amino group, $-NH_2$, at one end of the molecule, and a carboxyl group, $-COOH$, at the other end. However, each amino acid has a different R group.

▲ *Generalised amino acid*

Key Term

Dipeptide = two linked amino acids.

▼ Study point

Proteins carry out a range of biological activities and include enzymes, antibodies, hormones, carrier and transport proteins, as well as structural proteins.

The shape of one protein differs from that of all other types of protein.

Examiner tip

A change in a single amino acid in the polypeptide sequence can lead to a change in the shape of a protein and prevent it performing its function.

Formation of a peptide bond

Proteins are built up from a linear sequence of amino acids. The amino group of one amino acid reacts with the carboxyl group of another with the elimination of water. The bond that is formed is called a peptide bond and the resulting compound is a **dipeptide**.

▲ *Formation of a dipeptide*

Protein structure

Proteins are very large molecules and consist of long chains of many amino acids joined together. These chains are called polypeptides.

Primary structure

This is the sequence of amino acids in a polypeptide chain. As polypeptides have many of the 20 amino acids joined in any sequence, there are a huge number of possible combinations. Proteins differ from each other in the variety, numbers and order of their constituent amino acids. More commonly proteins consist of a number of polypeptide chains.

Secondary structure

The secondary structure is the shape that the polypeptide chain forms as a result of hydrogen bonding. This causes the long polypeptide chain to be twisted into a 3D shape. This spiral shape is known as the α helix.

Another less common arrangement is the β pleated sheet.

▶ *Structure of α helix*

▼ *Structure of β pleated sheet*

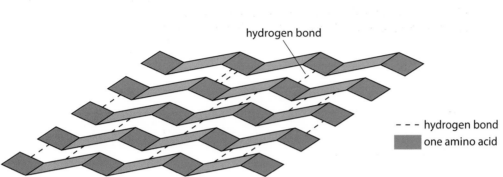

- - - hydrogen bond
▭ one amino acid

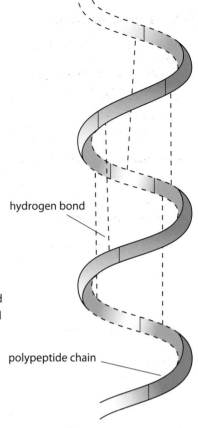

hydrogen bond

polypeptide chain

Tertiary structure

The α helix of the secondary protein structure can be folded and twisted to give a more complex, compact 3D structure. This is known as the tertiary structure. The shape is maintained by disulphide, ionic and hydrogen bonds, e.g. globular proteins.

▼ *Tertiary structure*

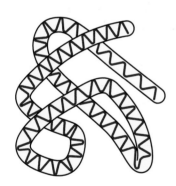

Examiner tip

Enzymes are tertiary proteins. The shape of the enzyme molecule is very precise and held in this exact shape by the bonds between amino acids in different parts of the chain.

Knowledge check

3

Match each level of the four protein structures with the appropriate description A–D.

A. Folding of the polypeptide into a 3-D shape.

B. α helix held together with hydrogen bonds.

C. The sequence of amino acids in the polypeptide chain.

D. The combination of two or more polypeptide chains in tertiary form, associated with a non-protein group.

▼ *Types of chemical bonds in a polypeptide*

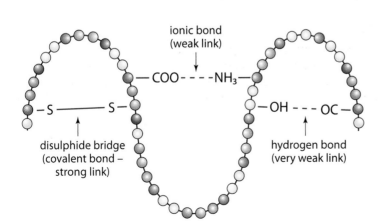

ionic bond
(weak link)

— COO - - - - NH₃—

—S———S—

disulphide bridge
(covalent bond –
strong link)

— OH - - - OC —

hydrogen bond
(very weak link)

Knowledge check

State the types of bonds that are formed as a result of condensation reactions between:

A. Two glucose molecules.

B. Fatty acids and glycerol.

C. Two amino acids.

Quaternary structure

The quaternary structure arises from a combination of two or more polypeptide chains in tertiary form. These are associated with non-protein groups and form large, complex molecules, e.g. haemoglobin.

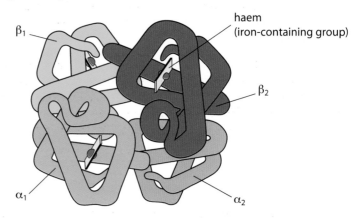

▲ Structure of haemoglobin

▼ Molecular structure of a protein

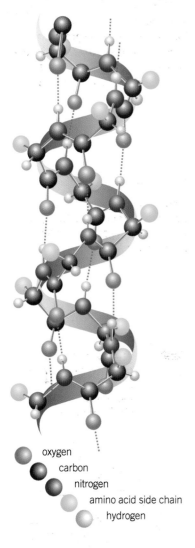

oxygen

carbon

nitrogen

amino acid side chain

hydrogen

Globular and fibrous proteins

The roles that proteins perform depend on their molecular shape. There are two basic types:

Fibrous proteins perform structural functions. They consist of polypeptides in parallel chains or sheets with numerous cross-linkages to form long fibres, for example keratin (in hair). Fibrous proteins are insoluble in water, strong and tough. Collagen provides tough properties needed in tendons. A single fibre consists of three polypeptide chains twisted around each other like a rope. These chains are linked by cross-bridges, making a very stable molecule.

Globular proteins perform a variety of different functions – enzymes, antibodies, plasma proteins and hormones. These proteins are compact and folded as spherical molecules. They are soluble in water. Haemoglobin consists of four folded polypeptide chains, at the centre of which is an iron-containing group called haem.

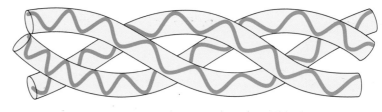

3 polypeptide strands tightly wound around one another

▲ Structure of fibrous protein e.g. collagen

Examiner tip

Biuret reagent consists of a mixture of sodium hydroxide and very dilute copper II sulphate solutions. In an examination you need only to refer to it as 'Biuret reagent'.

Test for protein – the Biuret test

To test a sample of a solution suspected of containing protein add a few drops of Biuret reagent. A purple colour indicates the presence of a protein. If no protein is present, the solution remains blue.

Water

Apart from providing a habitat for aquatic organisms, water plays an important role in plants and animals with key elements found in aqueous solution. Water acts as a medium for metabolic reactions. Water makes up between 65% and 95% by mass of most plants and animals. It is an important constituent of cells. In fact, about 70% of an individual human cell consists of water.

Although it is a simple molecule, water has some surprising properties. The most important property of water molecules is that they can 'stick together' by forming hydrogen bonds with other water molecules. Also, as it is a liquid, it provides a medium for molecules and ions to mix in. The hydrogen bonding of water molecules makes the molecules more difficult to separate and affects the physical properties of water.

Water as a solvent

Water is an excellent solvent. Because water has slightly positive and slightly negative parts, it will attract other charged particles, such as ions, and other polar molecules, such as glucose. This allows chemical reactions to take place in solution and since these chemicals dissolve in water, it acts a transport medium, e.g. in animals, blood transports many dissolved substances. In plants, water transports minerals in the xylem and sucrose in the phloem. Non-polar molecules such as lipids will not dissolve in water.

Examiner tip

A molecule gets its properties from its structure. Be prepared to explain how the properties of water enable it to carry out its many important roles in living organisms.

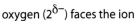

▼ *Water molecules arrange themselves around ions in solution*

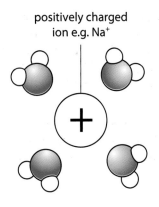

positively charged ion e.g. Na$^+$

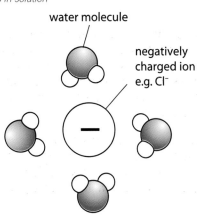

water molecule

negatively charged ion e.g. Cl$^-$

oxygen ($2^{\delta-}$) faces the ion

hydrogen ($^{\delta+}$) faces the ion

▼ Study point

Water molecules tend to be attracted to each other. Non-polar molecules such as lipids will not dissolve in water.

‹Link› The hydrophobic property of lipids is important in cell membranes. This is studied on page 36.

Thermal properties

Water has a high specific heat. A large amount of heat energy is needed to raise the temperature of water. This is because the hydrogen bonds between water molecules restrict their movement. This prevents large fluctuations in the temperature of water and this is particularly important in keeping the temperature of aquatic habitats stable so that organisms do not have to endure extremes of temperature. This also allows enzymes within the cells to work effectively.

Water has a high latent heat, i.e. a great deal of heat energy is needed to change it from a liquid to a vapour state. This is important, for example, in temperature control where heat is used for vaporisation of water when sweating. That is, the evaporation of water from a surface results in cooling.

hydrogen bond

▲ *Water molecules held together by hydrogen bonds*

Cohesion and surface tension

Water is a polar molecule and has no overall charge. The oxygen end of the molecule has a slight negative charge and the hydrogen end of the molecule has a slight positive charge. When two water molecules are in close contact their opposing charges attract each other forming a hydrogen bond. Individually the hydrogen bonds are weak but, because there are many of them, they stick together in a strong lattice framework. This sticking together of water molecules is called cohesion. This means that tall columns of water can be drawn up xylem vessels in tall trees.

At ordinary temperatures water has the highest surface tension of any liquid except mercury. In a pond the cohesion between water molecules produces surface tension so that the body of an insect such as the pond skater is supported.

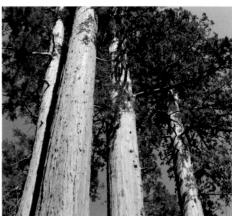

5

Knowledge check

Using one of the key words provided, in each case state why each of the following properties of water is important to living organisms:

Photosynthesis

Transport

Insulation

Cooling.

A. Universal solvent.

B. High latent heat of vaporisation.

C. It is transparent

D. In the solid state it is less dense.

Density

Water has a maximum density at 4°C. Water in its solid form (ice) is less dense than water and so floats on the surface and insulates the water under it. This reduces the tendency for large bodies of water to freeze completely and allows organisms to survive beneath it.

Water is transparent

This property allows light to pass through, enabling aquatic plants to photosynthesise effectively.

Inorganic ions

All the substances described so far are made up of molecules. All living organisms also need a variety of inorganic ions. They can be divided into two groups: micronutrients, which are needed in minute (trace) amounts, e.g. copper and zinc, and macronutrients, which are needed in small amounts. The roles of selected macronutrients are summarised as follows:

- Magnesium is an important constituent of chlorophyll and is therefore important in photosynthesis.
- Iron is a constituent of haemoglobin, which is important in the carriage of oxygen by red blood cells.
- Phosphate ions are used for making nucleotides, including ATP. They are also a constituent of phospholipids found in the plasma membrane.
- Calcium, together with phosphate, is an important structural component of bones and teeth.

Examiner tip

You are required to learn the functions of these four ions only.

Biological molecules

1 The following table lists some features of biological compounds. Tick the boxes in the table if the feature is found in carbohydrates, lipids or proteins. You can tick one, two or three boxes for each feature. (5)

Feature	Carbohydrate	Lipid	Protein
Can be saturated or unsaturated			
Contains peptide bonds			
Contains the elements carbon, hydrogen and oxygen			
Can contain disulphide bonds			
Cellulose and glucose are examples			

2 The diagram shows a molecule of α glucose:

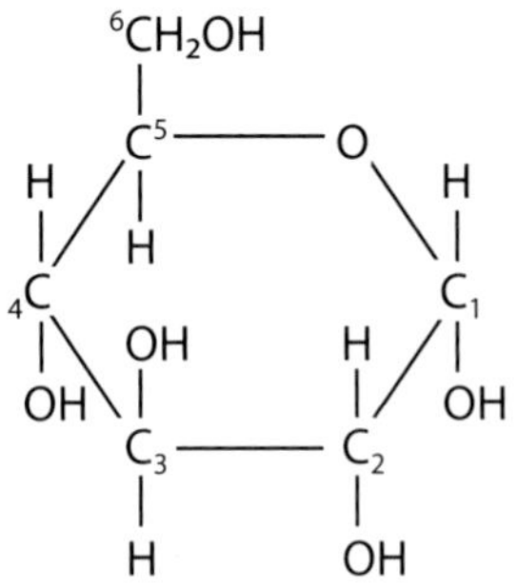

(a)(i) What name is given to this type of monosaccharide? (1)

  (ii) Name the disaccharide formed when two molecules of α glucose combine. (1)

 (iii) Name another product of this reaction. (1)

 (iv) Which carbon atoms form the glycosidic bond? (1)

(b)(i) Explain how the diagram for β glucose would differ from the above diagram. (1)

  (ii) Why are α and β glucose referred to as isomers? (1)

(c) Which of the two isomers form the polysaccharide cellulose in plants? (1)

(d) Apart from a few insects and some snails, the great majority of animals have failed to evolve an enzyme that will digest cellulose. Explain why cellulose is so much less reactive than other polysaccharides. (1)

(e) Explain one advantage that cellulose structure confers to the plant. (1)

9 The diagram shows the structure of a protein. The letters A to C indicate three types of bond found in a protein.

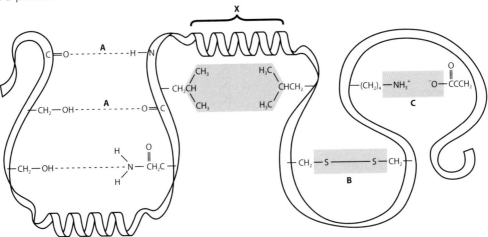

(a) State the names of the types of bond A to C. (3)

(b) The area marked X on the diagram forms part of the secondary structure of a protein.

  (i) State the name given to this form of secondary structure. (1)

  (ii) How is this form of secondary structure held together? (1)

  (iii) State the name of another form of secondary structure. (1)

(c) State the highest level of protein structure shown in the diagram. (1)

(d) A cellulose molecule is made up of a large number of monosaccharide units.

  (i) Name the monosaccharide and its form. (2)

  (ii) Explain how the structure of cellulose makes it suitable for use in plant cell walls. (2)

---

10 Inorganic ions are needed by living organisms. Give the functions of each of these four ions. (4)

Magnesium

Iron

Phosphate

Calcium

---

11 Describe the structure and function of lipids in plants and animals. (10)

BY1
Cell structure and organisation

Cells are the fundamental units of life where metabolic reactions occur. The detailed structure of a cell as revealed by the electron microscope is called its ultrastructure. Simple organisms consist of only one cell, that is, they are unicellular. More advanced organisms consist of many cells and are said to be multicellular, where different cells are specialised to carry out particular functions. Although cells have certain features in common, they also differ in their internal structure in order to perform these different functions. There are two distinct types of cells: prokaryote cells and eukaryote cells. Eukaryote cells have a distinct nucleus and possess membrane-bound organelles. Prokaryote cells, such as those of bacteria, have a simpler structure.

By the end of this topic you should be able to:

- Describe and interpret drawings and photographs of typical plant and animal cells as seen using the electron microscope.
- Recognise structures such as the nucleus, including the nuclear membrane and nucleolus, rough and smooth endoplasmic reticulum, mitochondria, chloroplasts, ribosomes, lysosomes, Golgi apparatus, plasma membrane, centrioles.
- Describe the functions of these structures.
- Describe how organelles are interrelated.
- Describe the similarities and differences between prokaryote and eukaryote cells.
- Explain the meaning of the terms 'tissue', 'organ' and 'system', stating examples in plants and animals.
- Describe the differences between plant and animal cells.

Topic contents

YOU SHOULD KNOW ›››

››› the structure and functions of organelles

››› how to recognise and identify organelles from electron micrographs

››› the role of a cell by looking at the number and size of organelles it contains

››› that organelles are often inter-related through their functions

▼ **Study point**

Very small units of measurements are used to measure objects such as organelles. The units of length relevant to cell studies are µm, micrometre = one millionth of a metre and nm, nanometre = one thousand millionth of a metre!

Examiner tip

The cell is a 3D structure. An electron micrograph may show mitochondria as circular or sausage-shaped, as they are cut in different planes.

▼ *EM of nucleus*

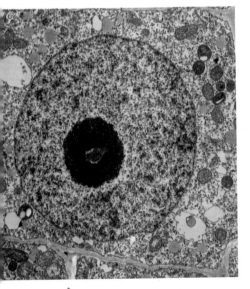

◆ **Link** ▶ See nucleic acids on page 58.

Cell structure

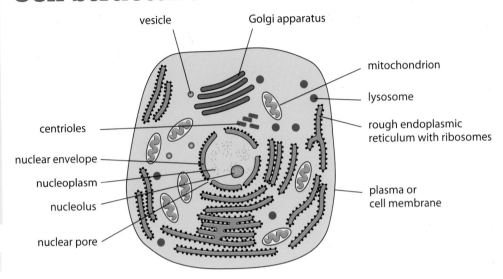

vesicle — Golgi apparatus — mitochondrion — lysosome — rough endoplasmic reticulum with ribosomes — plasma or cell membrane — centrioles — nuclear envelope — nucleoplasm — nucleolus — nuclear pore

▲ *Ultrastructure of a typical animal cell as seen with an electron microscope*

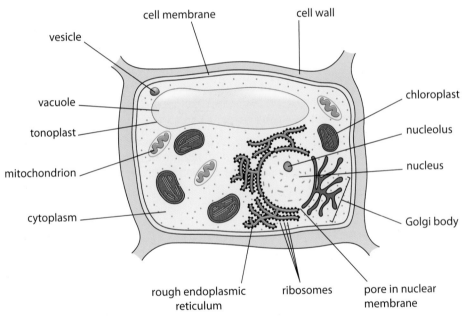

cell membrane — cell wall — vesicle — vacuole — tonoplast — mitochondrion — cytoplasm — chloroplast — nucleolus — nucleus — Golgi body — rough endoplasmic reticulum — ribosomes — pore in nuclear membrane

▲ *Ultrastructure of a typical plant cell as seen with an electron microscope*

Eukaryote cells contain membranous organelles which are enclosed areas within the cytoplasm. This has the advantage that any potentially harmful chemicals and/or enzymes can be isolated. Membranes also provide a large surface area for the attachment of enzymes involved in metabolic processes, as well as providing a transport system within the cell. The structure and functions of the organelles found in eukaryote cells are described below.

Nucleus

This is the most prominent feature in the cell. It is usually spherical and between 10 and 20 µm in diameter. Its function is to control the cell's activities and to retain the chromosomes. The nucleus is made up of a number of components:

- It is bounded by a double membrane called the nuclear membrane or envelope. Its outer membrane is continuous with the endoplasmic reticulum. The membrane also has pores in it to allow the passage of large molecules such as mRNA out of the nucleus.
- The granular jelly-like material within the nucleus is called the nucleoplasm. It contains chromatin, which is made up of coils of DNA bound to protein. During cell division the chromatin condenses to form the chromosomes.
- Within the nucleus is a small spherical body called a nucleolus. Its function is to manufacture RNA, which is needed to make ribosomes.

Mitochondria

Mitochondria are rod-shaped and 1–10 µm in length. They are made up of the following structures:

- A double membrane separated by a narrow fluid-filled inter-membrane space. The inner membrane is folded inwards to form extensions called cristae.
- An organic matrix containing numerous chemical compounds including protein, lipids and traces of DNA that allows the mitochondria to control the production of their own protein.

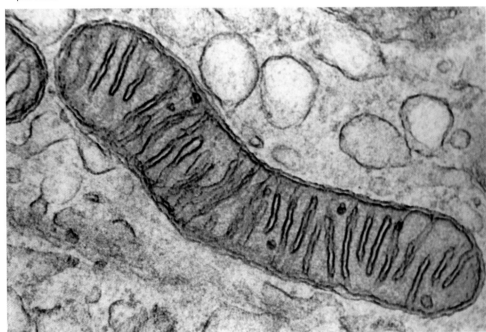

Mitochondria are the sites of aerobic respiration in the cell. Some of the reactions take place in the matrix while others occur on the inner membrane. The cristae provide a large surface area for the attachment of enzymes involved in respiration.

The function of mitochondria is to produce the energy-carrier molecule, ATP. Metabolically active cells such as muscle cells need a plentiful supply of ATP. They are found to contain large numbers of mitochondria, reflecting the high metabolic activity taking place there.

Endoplasmic reticulum (ER)

This consists of an elaborate system of parallel double membranes forming flattened sacs. The fluid-filled spaces between the membranes are called cisternae. The ER is connected with the nuclear membrane and may link to the Golgi body. The cavities are interconnected and this system allows the transport of materials throughout the cell.

How Science Works

Scientists worked out the function of a cell from a study of its ultrastructure and its location. For example, epithelial cells use a lot of energy in the process of absorbing substances from the intestines by active transport and so contain large numbers of mitochondria.

◀ *Mitochondrion*

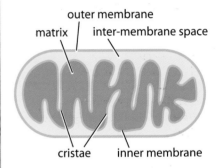

Basic structure of a mitochondrion

6

Knowledge check

Match the structures 1–4 with the descriptions of their functions A–D.

1. Ribosome
2. Nucleus
3. Mitochondria
4. Golgi body

A. Contains the genetic material.
B. Site of protein synthesis.
C. Modifies proteins after their production.
D. Site of respiration.

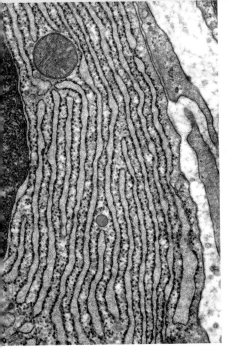

Endoplasmic reticulum

▼ **Study point**

The Golgi body receives, sorts and delivers proteins and lipids.

Lysosomes carry out recycling and refuse disposal. They remove worn out organelles and potentially dangerous material such as bacteria. They reuse the useful components and dispose of the remainder.

▼ *Golgi body*

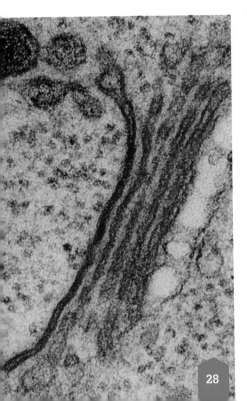

There are two types of ER:

- Rough ER has ribosomes on the outer surface. The rough ER functions in transporting proteins made by the ribosomes. Rough ER is present in large amounts in cells that make enzymes that may be secreted out of the cell.

- Smooth ER has membranes that lack ribosomes. These are concerned with the synthesis and transport of lipids.

Cells that need to store large quantities of carbohydrates, proteins and fats have extensive ER. Such cells include liver and secretory cells.

Ribosomes

Ribosomes are found in both prokaryote and eukaryote cells but are smaller in the former. They may occur singly in the cytoplasm or are associated with the rough ER. Ribosomes are made up of one large and one small sub-unit. They are manufactured in the nucleolus from ribosomal RNA and protein. They are important in protein synthesis.

Golgi body

This is similar in structure to ER but is more compact. The Golgi body is formed by rough ER being pinched off at the ends to form small vesicles. A number of these vesicles then fuse together to form the Golgi body. Proteins are transported in the vesicles and are modified and packaged in the Golgi body. For example, proteins may be combined with carbohydrates to make glycoproteins.

At the other end of the Golgi body vesicles can be pinched off and the products secreted by exocytosis when the vesicle moves to and fuses with the cell membrane.

Other functions of the Golgi body include:

- Producing secretory enzymes.
- Secreting carbohydrates, e.g. for the formation of plant cell walls.
- Producing glycoprotein.
- Transporting and storing lipids.
- Forming lysosomes.

Lysosomes

Lysosomes are small vacuoles formed when portions of the Golgi body are pinched off. They contain and isolate these potentially harmful digestive enzymes from the remainder of the cell. They can also release these enzymes and destroy worn out organelles in the cell. Digestion is carried out in the membrane-lined vacuole into which several lysosomes may discharge their contents.

They can also digest material that has been taken into the cell, e.g. white blood cells engulf bacteria by phagocytosis and the lysosomes discharge their contents into the vesicle so formed and digest the bacterium.

Centrioles

Centrioles are found in all animal cells and most protoctists but are absent from the cells of higher plants. Centrioles are located just outside the nucleus in a distinct region of the cytoplasm known as the centrosome. A centriole consists of two hollow cylinders positioned at right angles to one another. During cell division centrioles divide and move to opposite poles of the cell where they synthesise the microtubules of the spindle.

Organelles are interrelated

Although organelles are described separately, their functions within the cell are often related.

- Ribosomes are produced in the nucleolus and take up their positions on the rough ER.

- The pores in the nuclear membrane allow mRNA molecules to leave the nucleus and attach to the ribosomes on the rough ER.

- The process of protein synthesis takes place on the ribosomes with the production of proteins in their primary structure.

- The polypeptides are modified in the Golgi body and converted into their tertiary structure.

- The enzymes are packaged into secretory vesicles and transported to the membrane through which secretion takes place.

Plant cells are eukaryotic cells. They have a distinct nucleus and membrane-bound organelles, such as mitochondria. However, in addition they possess other structures not present in animal cells.

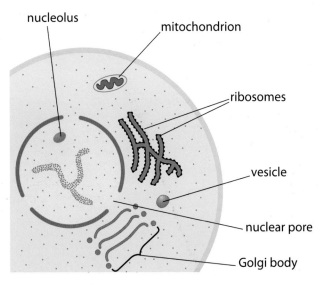

▲ *Nucleus, RER and Golgi body*

Chloroplast

Chloroplasts are found in the cells of photosynthesising tissue.

- Each chloroplast is surrounded by a double plasma membrane or envelope.

- The stroma is fluid-filled and contains ribosomes, lipid, circular DNA and other structures such as starch.

- Within the stroma are many flattened sacs called thylakoids. A stack of thylakoids is called a granum. Each granum consists of between two and a hundred of these closed, parallel, flattened sacs. The photosynthetic pigments such as chlorophyll are found within the thylakoids. This arrangement produces a large surface area for trapping light energy.

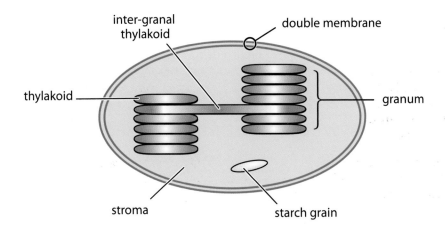

▲ *Basic structure of a chloroplast*

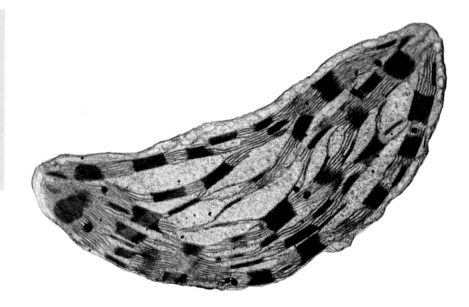

▶ *Chloroplast*

▼ Study points

Not all plant cells contain chloroplasts. For example, root cells, being underground, do not photosynthesise.

Animal cells contain vacuoles but these are small, temporary vesicles and may occur in large numbers.

Turgid cells provide mechanical support to soft plant tissues and keep them upright. This is particularly important in young seedlings.

 More detail on the role of the cell wall is found on page 40.

Vacuole

Plant cells have a large permanent vacuole which consists of a fluid-filled sac bounded by a single membrane, the tonoplast. Vacuoles contain cell sap, a storage site for chemicals such as glucose, and provide an osmotic system which functions in support of young tissues.

Apart from acting as storage areas for substances such as glucose and amino acids, water enters the vacuole by osmosis with the result that the vacuole expands pushing the cell contents against the cell wall. When the cell can take in no more water it is said to be turgid.

Cellulose cell wall

The cell wall consists of cellulose microfibrils embedded in a polysaccharide matrix. The cell wall has the following functions:

- It is fully permeable to water and substances in solution. When the water-filled vacuole pushes the cell contents against the cell wall, the cell wall must be strong enough to resist this expansion to enable the cell to become turgid.
- As the cellulose microfibrils are very strong, the cell wall provides mechanical strength.

It enables cells to connect with each other through narrow pores or pits through which strands of cytoplasm (plasmodesmata) pass. This allows the exchange of materials between one cell and the next.

Differences between plant and animal cells

Plant cells have all the structures found in animal cells plus some additional features:

Plant cells	Animal cells
Cell wall surrounding a membrane	No cell wall, membrane only
Chloroplasts present	Chloroplasts never present
Large permanent single, central vacuole filled with cell sap	Small, temporary vacuoles scattered throughout the cell
No centriole	Centriole
Plasmodesmata	No plasmodesmata
Starch grains used for storage	Glycogen granules used for storage

Levels of organisation
Differentiation and specialisation

Single-celled organisms carry out all life functions within a single cell. Multicellular organisms need specialised cells, forming tissues and organs, to carry out particular functions. As they develop, each cell becomes specialised in structure to suit the role it will perform.

Some cells remain unspecialised or undifferentiated and function as 'packing' cells, for example parenchyma cells in plants. Other cells can **differentiate** in a number of ways involving one, two or all three of the following changes:

- The shape of the cell – nerve cells become long and thin to carry impulses.
- The number of a particular organelle – cells which carry out photosynthesis contain a large number of chloroplasts.
- The contents of the cell – red blood cells are packed with the protein haemoglobin.

Tissues

Cells that differentiate in the same way are grouped together into tissues. A tissue consists of a collection of specialised cells of the same type, working together to carry out a particular function, for example epithelial tissue which is sheets of cells that line the surface of organs in animals. These cells often have a protective or secretory function.

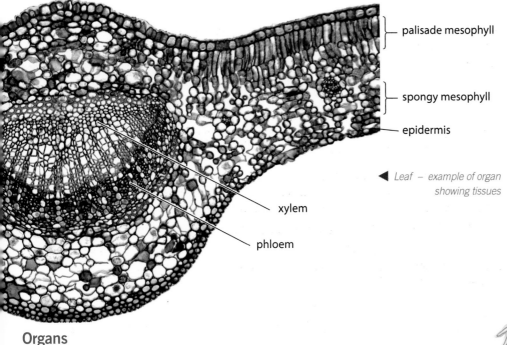

palisade mesophyll

spongy mesophyll

epidermis

xylem

phloem

◄ *Leaf – example of organ showing tissues*

Organs

An organ is a part of the body which forms a structural and functional unit and is made up of more than one tissue. For example, the eye is an organ of sight.

Systems

A system is a collection of organs which carry out a particular function. For example, the digestive system, the reproductive system.

Organisms

All the systems of the body work together, making up an organism.

Key Terms

Differentiation = cells become specialised to carry out a particular role.

7

Knowledge check

Match the structures 1–3 with the descriptions of their functions A–C.

1. Chloroplast
2. Cell wall
3. Golgi body

A. Provides mechanical support.
B. Site of photosynthesis.
C. Modifies proteins after their production.

▼ *Body system – circulatory*

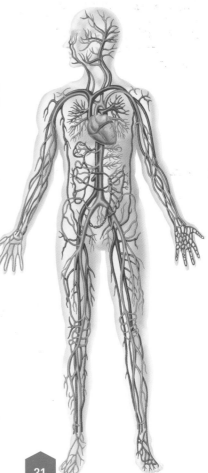

Prokaryote and eukaryote cells and viruses

Prokaryote and eukaryote cells

So far we have studied the structure and organisation of eukaryote cells. Eukaryotic cells probably evolved from prokaryote cells around 1000 million years ago. Prokaryote cells do have a simpler structure and were probably the first forms of life on Earth. An example of a prokaryote cell is a bacterium. Eukaryote cells are typical of the great majority of organisms including all animals and plants.

Examiner tip

Be prepared to draw and label a prokaryote cell and to make a comparison with an eukaryote cell.

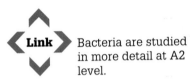

Link Bacteria are studied in more detail at A2 level.

Prokaryotic cells	Eukaryotic cells
Found in bacteria and blue-green algae	Found in plants, animals, fungi and protoctists
No membrane-bound organelles	Membrane-bound organelles
Ribosomes are smaller	DNA located on chromosomes
DNA lies free in the cytoplasm	Distinct membrane-bound nucleus
No nuclear membrane or ER	Ribosomes are larger
Cell wall containing murein	Cell wall in plants made of cellulose

Viruses

Viruses are an unusual life-form, very different from any other organism. They are extremely small and can only be seen using an electron microscope. They can be called 'non-cells' as they have no cytoplasm, no organelles and no chromosomes. Outside a living cell a virus exists as an inert 'virion'. When they invade a cell they are able to take over the cell's metabolism and multiply within the host cell. Each virus particle is made up of a core of nucleic acid surrounded by a protein coat, the capsid.

Most viruses are found in animal cells and those attacking bacteria (bacteriophages) have the nucleic acid DNA. Other animal and plant viruses contain RNA. A widely studied virus is T2 phage, a bacteriophage, which infects the bacterium *Escherichia coli* (*E.coli*).

Viruses cause a variety of infectious diseases in humans, animals and plants.

Bacterium diagram labels: cell membrane, DNA, cytoplasm, cell wall, mesosome (site of respiration), ribosome, plasmid, flagellum

▲ *Bacterium*

Examiner tip
This is all the detail you need to know about viruses.

▶ *A virus*

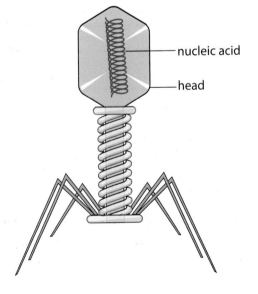

nucleic acid

head

Cell structure and organisation

1   Cells are classified as either prokaryotic or eukaryotic. The table lists certain features of each type of cell.

(a)   Indicate by placing a tick in the box if the characteristic is present. (4)

Feature	Prokaryotic cell	Eukaryotic plant cell
Chromosomes		
Respiration in mesosomes		
Membrane-bound organelles		
Ribosomes present		

(b) State one other difference between a prokaryotic cell and a eukaryotic plant cell. (1)

2   Complete the following table to compare the structure of plant cells, bacteria and viruses, by placing a tick in the appropriate boxes. Each row may have one, two or three ticks. (6)

Structural feature	Plant cells	Bacteria	Viruses
May contain mitochondria			
Have cell walls			
May contain DNA			
May contain chloroplasts			
Do not have a membrane-bound nucleus			
May have plasmids			

3   The diagram (right) is of a plant cell as seen under an electron microscope:

(a)(i) Name structures A to E. (5)

(ii) Describe the functions of A, C, and E. (3)

(b)   Name the carbohydrates in the cell which are found:

(i) In the cell wall. (1)

(ii) As a storage compound in the cell. (1)

(iii) As a component of ribosomes. (1)

(c)   State two ways in which a plant cell would differ from an animal cell. (2)

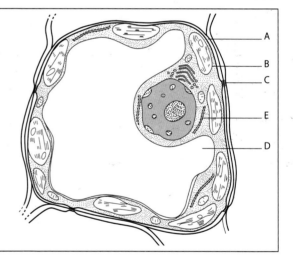

4   Plant and animal cells are described as being eukaryotic. Bacteria are prokaryotic organisms.

Complete the table by placing a tick if the feature is present or a cross if it is absent. (6)

Feature	Bacterial cell	Leaf cell	Muscle cell
Cell wall			
Large permanent vacuole			
Nuclear membrane			
Chloroplasts			
Mesosomes			
Mitochondria			

(b)(i) State what is meant by the term tissue. (2)

(ii) Which of the following is classified as a tissue: sperm, muscle, leaf? (1)

5 The diagram shows the structure of a chloroplast:

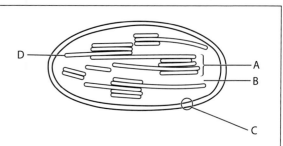

(a) Name the structures labelled A to D. (4)

(b) One organic compound, which is found in the internal membranes of the chloroplast, never occurs in any other plant or animal organelle. Name this compound. (1)

6 The diagram shows part of a cell that secretes a hormone into the blood stream:

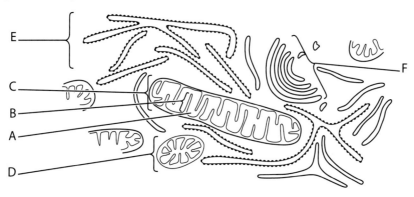

(a) Name structures A and B. (2)

(b) Explain the functions of structures E and F. (4)

(c) Suggest why this type of cell is likely to contain large numbers of structure C. (2)

(d) Labels C and D show the same type of organelle. Explain why they differ in appearance. (1)

7 (a) Which two chemical components make up a ribosome? (2)

(b) On which membranous structure in the cell are ribosomes found? (1)

(c) What is the function of ribosomes? (1)

(d) State precisely where in the cell ribosomes are synthesised. (1)

8 Complete the table by ticking one box in each case to show which of the organelles are described by the statements listed. (7)

Statement	Smooth endoplasmic reticulum	Mitochondria	Golgi body	Rough endoplasmic reticulum
Surrounded by a double membrane				
Produces glycoprotein				
Buds off lysosomes				
Manufactures enzymes				
Most abundant at sites of active transport				
Abundant in cells secreting lipids				
Closely associated with ribosomes				

9 Describe the structure and function of the rough endoplasmic reticulum, Golgi body and lysosomes. (10)

Cell membranes and transport

The organelles and structures within a cell require a variety of materials in order to carry out their functions. All cells are surrounded by a cell-surface membrane or plasma membrane which controls the exchange of materials, such as nutrients and waste products, between the cell and its environment

The membrane acts as a boundary that separates the living cell from its non-living surroundings. The membrane also controls which substances pass into and out of the cell.

By the end of this topic you should be able to:

- Describe the fluid mosaic model of membrane structure and explain its role in the cell.
- Outline the role of the chemical components in membranes.
- Describe and explain how molecules enter and leave cells by the processes of: diffusion, facilitated diffusion, osmosis, active transport, endocytosis and exocytosis.

Topic contents

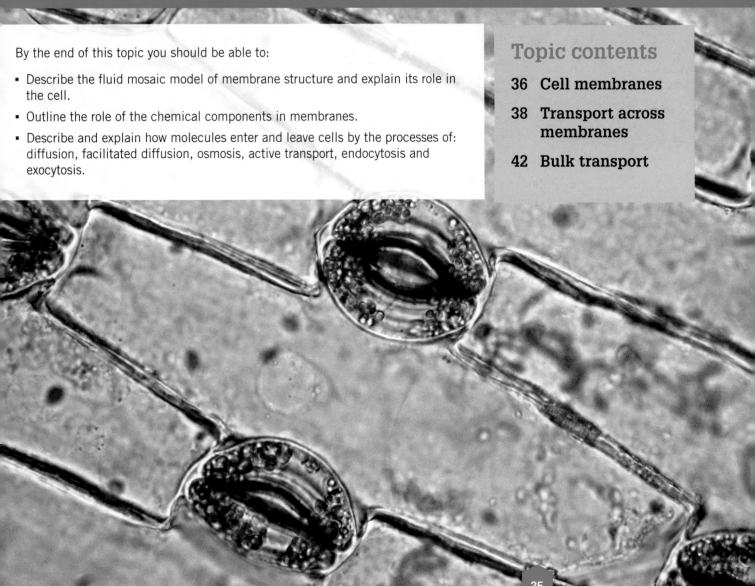

Cell membranes

The cell membrane is made up almost entirely of proteins and phospholipids.

Phospholipids

They are important components of cell-surface membranes for the following reasons:

- Phospholipids can form bilayers with one sheet of phospholipid forming over another.
- One layer of phospholipids has its hydrophilic heads pointing inwards and interacts with the water inside the cell cytoplasm.
- The other layer of phospholipids has its hydrophilic heads pointing outwards interacting with the water that surrounds the cell.
- The hydrophobic tails of both phospholipid layers point to the centre of the membrane.
- This phospholipid bilayer forms the basis of membrane structure.

The phospholipid component allows lipid-soluble molecules to enter and leave the cell but prevents water-soluble molecules from doing so.

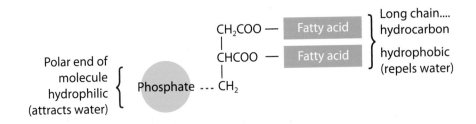

▲ Structure of a phospholipid

Proteins

In the membrane the proteins are arranged randomly in contrast to the more regular pattern of phospholipids. There are two ways in which they are embedded in the membrane:

- Extrinsic proteins, which occur on the surface of the bilayer or partly embedded in it. They provide structural support. They also form recognition sites by identifying cells.
- Intrinsic proteins, which extend across both layers. Some of these act as carriers transporting water-soluble substances across the membrane. Others allow active transport across the membrane by forming channels for ions.

The diagram shows the way in which the phospholipids and proteins are arranged in the membrane. This arrangement is called the fluid mosaic model and was proposed by Singer and Nicholson in 1972.

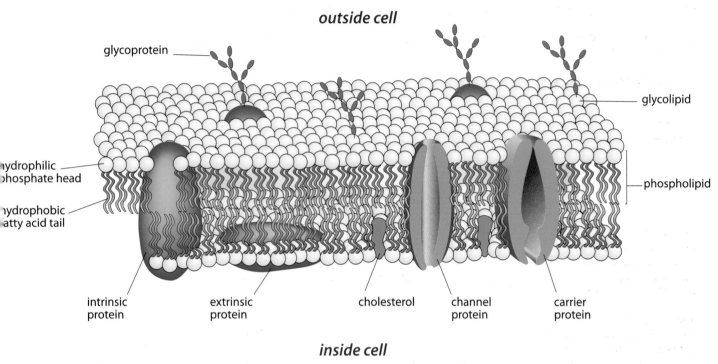

outside cell

glycoprotein

glycolipid

hydrophilic phosphate head

phospholipid

hydrophobic fatty acid tail

intrinsic protein

extrinsic protein

cholesterol

channel protein

carrier protein

inside cell

▲ *Plasma membrane structure*

The model is referred to as the 'fluid mosaic' model because the individual phospholipid molecules can move relative to one another (fluid) and the proteins embedded in the bilayer vary in shape, size and pattern (mosaic).

Cholesterol is also found in animal cells. It fits between the phospholipid molecules, increasing the rigidity and stability of the membrane. Glycolipids (lipids that have combined with polysaccharide) are also found in the outer layer of the membrane and are thought to be involved in cell-to-cell recognition. Glycoproteins also stick out of some membranes.

The membrane as a barrier

Lipid-soluble substances move through the membrane via the phospholipid part. It prevents the entry or exit of water-soluble substances. The latter, pass through special protein molecules, which form water-filled channels across the membrane. The cell surface membrane is selectively permeable to water and some solutes. Lipid-soluble substances can move through the cell membrane more easily than water-soluble substances.

Small, uncharged molecules, such as oxygen and carbon dioxide, pass freely through the membrane as they are soluble in the lipid part.

Lipid-soluble molecules such as glycerol can pass through the membrane.

The hydrophobic core of the membrane impedes the transport of ions and polar molecules.

Charged particles (ions) and relatively large molecules, such as glucose, cannot diffuse across the non-polar centre of the phospholipid bilayer because they are relatively insoluble in lipid. Intrinsic proteins assist such particles to pass in or out of the cell by a passive process called facilitated diffusion.

Examiner tip
This is a difficult concept. The hydrophobic core of the membrane impedes the transport of ions and polar molecules. These require specific proteins to help them across.

Transport across membranes

Diffusion

Diffusion is an example of passive transport. Diffusion is the movement of molecules or ions from a region where they are in high concentration to a region of lower concentration until they are equally distributed. Ions and molecules are always in a state of random movement but if they are highly concentrated in one area there will be a net movement away from that area until equilibrium is reached or until there is a uniform distribution.

The rate of diffusion is affected by:

- The concentration gradient. The greater the difference in the concentration of molecules in two areas, the greater the rate.
- The distance of travel over which diffusion takes place. The shorter the distance between two areas, the greater the rate.
- The surface area of the membrane – the larger the area, the quicker the rate.
- The thickness of the exchange surface. The thinner the membrane, the greater the rate.
- An increase in temperature results in an increase in rate since there is an increase in kinetic energy.

Diffusion is proportional to: $\dfrac{\text{Surface area} \times \text{difference in concentration}}{\text{Length of the diffusion path}}$

Examiner tip

Although the equation opposite is a good general guide to the rate of diffusion, other factors also affect the rate. These include the composition and the number of pores in the membrane, the size and nature of the diffusing molecule. Fat-soluble molecules diffuse faster than water-soluble molecules, and polar molecules diffuse faster than non-polar ones.

Facilitated diffusion

Charged particles or ions and large molecules such as glucose cannot pass through the cell membrane because they are relatively insoluble in lipid.

Facilitated diffusion is a special form of diffusion that allows faster movement of these molecules. It is a passive process and occurs down a concentration gradient. However, it occurs at specific points on the plasma membrane where there are special protein molecules.

These proteins are of two types:

- Channel proteins – consist of pores lined with polar groups allowing charged ions to pass through. (As the channel is hydrophilic, water-soluble substances can pass through.) As each channel protein is specific for one type of ion, each protein will only let one particular ion through. They can also open and close according to the needs of the cell.
- Carrier proteins allow diffusion across the membrane of larger polar molecules such as sugars and amino acids. A particular molecule attaches to the carrier protein at its binding site and causes the carrier protein to change its shape, releasing the molecule through the membrane.

▼ **Study points**

Using the term 'short diffusion path' in the correct context will impress.

All particles are in constant motion due to the kinetic energy they possess.

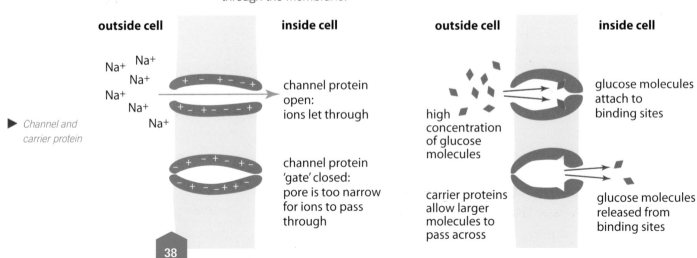

▶ Channel and carrier protein

outside cell **inside cell**

Na⁺ Na⁺ Na⁺ Na⁺ Na⁺ Na⁺

channel protein open: ions let through

channel protein 'gate' closed: pore is too narrow for ions to pass through

outside cell **inside cell**

high concentration of glucose molecules

carrier proteins allow larger molecules to pass across

glucose molecules attach to binding sites

glucose molecules released from binding sites

Active transport

Unlike the processes described so far, active transport is an energy-requiring process in which ions and molecules are moved across membranes against a concentration gradient.

The features of active transport are:

- Ions and molecules can move in the opposite direction to that in which diffusion occurs. That is, they move against a concentration gradient.
- The energy for active transport is supplied by ATP, and anything that affects the respiratory process will affect active transport.
- The process occurs through the carrier proteins that span the membrane.

Processes involving active transport include: protein synthesis, muscle contraction, nerve impulse transmission, and mineral salts uptake by plant roots.

Active transport of a single molecule or ion occurs as follows:

- The molecule or ion combines with a specific carrier protein.
- ATP transfers a phosphate group to the carrier protein on the inside of the membrane.
- As a result, the carrier protein changes shape and carries the molecule or ion to the inside of the membrane.
- The molecule or ion is released to the inside of the membrane and the carrier protein returns to its original shape.

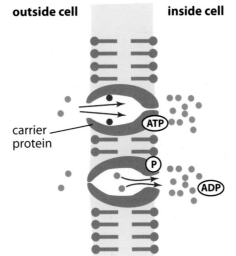

outside cell　　　　**inside cell**

carrier protein

ATP

P

ADP

▶ *Carrier proteins change shape when transporting a molecule across the membrane*

Active transport and respiratory inhibitors

Active transport will not take place in the presence of a respiratory inhibitor such as cyanide.

The graph below shows that at higher concentration differences a plateau is reached when the carrier proteins are saturated. The rate of uptake is affected with the addition of a respiratory inhibitor. Active transport must be taking place as the process requires ATP.

▼ *Inhibition of active transport*

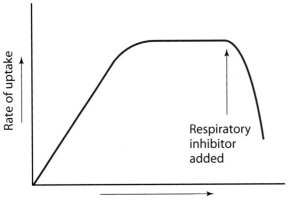

Rate of uptake

Respiratory inhibitor added

Concentration difference across membrane

Key Term

Solute = any substance that is dissolved in a solvent.
Solutes and solvents form a solution.

Study points

Membranes are selectively or partially permeable, that is, they are permeable to water molecules and some other small molecules but not to larger molecules. Osmosis is a specialised form of diffusion involving only water molecules.

Biologists use the term water potential (WP) ψ(psi) to describe the tendency of water molecules to leave a system.

Examiner tip
The highest value of water potential, that is, of pure water, is zero. All other values are negative.

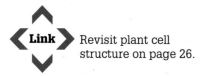

‹ Link › Revisit plant cell structure on page 26.

Osmosis

Most cell membranes are permeable to water and certain solutes only. In biological systems osmosis is a special case of diffusion which involves the movement of water molecules only.

Osmosis is defined as: the passage of water, from a region of higher water potential, to a region of lower water potential, through a partially permeable membrane.

Water potential (WP) is the pressure created by water molecules and is measured in kilopascals (kPa). Pure water has a water potential of zero. The addition of a **solute** to pure water will lower the water potential. That is the solution has a negative value.

Pure water has the highest water potential of zero. This is because where there is a high concentration of water molecules, they have a greater potential energy. That is, the water molecules are completely free to move about. When a solute, such as sugar, is dissolved in water, there are proportionally fewer water molecules to move about and the water potential of the solution is lowered. All water potentials (except that of pure water) have a negative value. The more concentrated the solution, the more negative the water potential. That is, the fewer free water molecules there are.

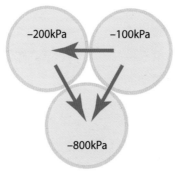

water moves from a high WP to a lower or more negative WP

▲ *Water movement between cells*

Osmosis and plant cells

Water entering a plant cell by osmosis causes the vacuole to expand and push the cytoplasm against the cell wall. The cell wall can expand only by a limited degree; therefore pressure builds up on it resisting the entry of more water. The cell is said to be turgid.

Turgor and plasmolysis

- If the WP of the external solution is lower than the solution inside the cell, it is said to be hypertonic and water flows out of the cell.
- If the WP of the external solution is higher than the solution inside the cell, it is said to be hypotonic and water flows into the cell.
- If the cell has the same solute concentration as the surrounding solution, the external solution is isotonic with that of the cell.
- When a plant cell is placed in a hypertonic solution it loses water by osmosis. The vacuole shrinks and the cytoplasm will draw away from the cell wall. This process is called plasmolysis and, when complete, the cell is said to be flaccid.
- The point at which the cell membrane just begins to move away from the cell wall is said to be the point of incipient plasmolysis.

A plant cell will gain water if placed in a hypotonic solution and will continue to take in water until prevented by the opposing wall pressure. The pressure potential rises until it is equal and opposite to the solute potential. In theory the water potential is now zero and when the cell cannot take in any more water, it is said to be turgid. The state of turgor is important in plants, particularly young seedlings. It supports them and maintains their shape and form.

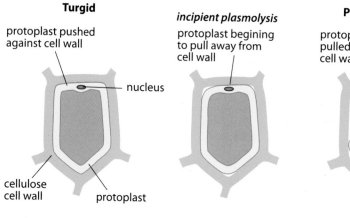

Turgid
protoplast pushed against cell wall
— nucleus

cellulose cell wall
protoplast

incipient plasmolysis
protoplast begining to pull away from cell wall

Plasmolysed
protoplast completely pulled away from cell wall

▲ *Turgid and plasmolysed cells*

▼ **Study points**

Don't forget to include in your revision any practical work connected with water potential and plasmolysis of cells.

An animal cell reacts differently from a plant cell when placed in hypertonic and hypotonic solutions as it has no cell wall.

In plant cells the following equation is used to describe the relationship between the forces:

$$\psi = \psi_s + \psi_p$$

water potential = solute potential + pressure potential

- The presence of solute molecules in the vacuole of a plant cell lowers the water potential.

- The concentration of dissolved substances inside the cell vacuole is called the solute potential.

- When water enters a plant cell vacuole by osmosis a hydrostatic pressure is set up and pushes outwards on the cell wall. As the outward pressure builds up, the cell wall develops an opposing force called the pressure potential. The pressure potential is usually positive.

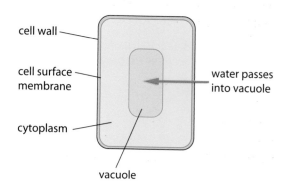

cell wall
cell surface membrane
cytoplasm
vacuole

water passes into vacuole

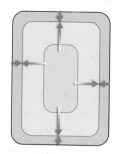

as water enters the cell, the rigid cell wall develops an opposing pressure potential

▲ *Solute and pressure potential*

Knowledge check

8

Link the processes 1–4 with the following statements A–D.

1. Diffusion
2. Facilitated diffusion
3. Osmosis
4. Active transport.

A. Does not take place in presence of cyanide.
B. Does not require cell energy.
C. A special form of diffusion involving water molecules.
D. Movement involves membrane proteins.

(Hint – some statements may be applicable to more than one process.)

Osmosis and animal cells

As it has no cell wall, an animal cell is affected differently. The diagram shows that if red blood cells are placed in distilled water, water enters by osmosis and bursts them. This is called haemolysis.

If red blood cells are placed into strong salt solution, water passes out of the cells and the cells shrink.

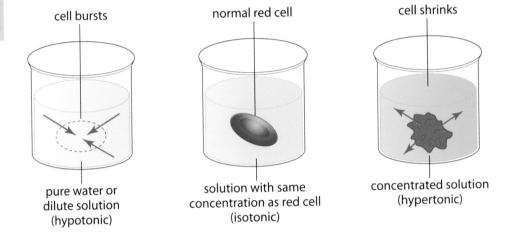

▶ Osmosis and animal cells

cell bursts

normal red cell

cell shrinks

pure water or dilute solution (hypotonic)

solution with same concentration as red cell (isotonic)

concentrated solution (hypertonic)

Bulk transport

Up to this point we have considered the ways in which the membrane transports individual molecules or ions. There are also processes where the cell transports materials in bulk into the cell (endocytosis) or out of the cell (exocytosis).

- Endocytosis involves the engulfing of the material by the plasma membrane bringing it into the cell inside a vesicle. There are two types of endocytosis:
  - Phagocytosis is the process by which the cell can obtain solid materials that are too large to be taken in by diffusion or active transport. A lysosome fuses with the vesicle formed, enzymes digest the solid material and the products are absorbed into the cytoplasm. Phagocytes (white blood cells) destroy bacteria and remove cell debris by phagocytosis.
  - Pinocytosis is the entry of liquid by the same mechanism as phagocytosis, except that the vesicles produced are smaller.
- Exocytosis refers to substances leaving the cell after being transported through the cytoplasm in a vesicle. Digestive enzymes are often secreted in this way.

▶ Phagocytosis and exocytosis

phagocytosis

endocytosis

vesicle

plasma membrane

bacterium engulfed

bacterium

lysosomes empty their enzymes into vesicle

bacterium digested

product released

secretory product e.g. enzyme

Golgi apparatus

Cell membrane and transport

1 (a) The diagram represents a model of a section through a cell surface membrane, as proposed by Singer and Nicholson:

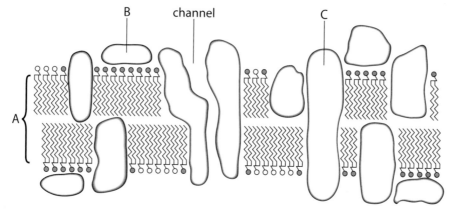

(i) State the name given to this model and give reasons why it is so-called. (3)

(ii) Name the structures labelled A, B and C. (3)

(iii) Describe the function of the channel shown in the diagram. (1)

(b) Some molecules are transported across the membrane by active transport. What is meant by the term 'active transport'? (2)

(c) State three functions of the cell surface membrane. (2)

2 Different compounds are transported through the plasma membrane into the cell in different ways. Complete the table to show how the three types of compound in the first column enter the cell. In the last column, list one factor which could alter the rate of entry of the compound at constant temperature. (9)

Type of compound	Method of transport into cell	Component of the membrane through which it passes	Factor affecting rate of transport
Lipid soluble			
Water soluble in high external concentration			
Water soluble in very low external concentration			

3 The following graphs show the effect of an increasing concentration gradient on the rate of uptake of substances across the cell membrane. The effect of adding a respiratory inhibitor on the rate of uptake is also shown. For each graph name the type of uptake involved and give reasons for your choice. (9)

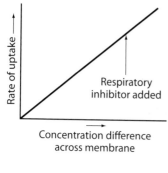

Process A

Process B

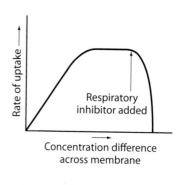

Process C

4 Each statement in the table applies to one or more of the three ways in which materials in solution can enter a cell across the plasma membrane. Complete the table by placing a tick in the appropriate box or boxes. (9)

Statement	Diffusion	Facilitated diffusion	Active transport
Substance dissolves in lipid part of membrane			
Will not take place in the presence of cyanide			
Movement involves membrane proteins			
Does not require cell energy			
Rate is proportional to concentration gradient across membrane			
Due to random movement of molecules in external solution			
Membrane proteins act as pumps			

5 (a) Define the term 'water potential'. (1)

(b) A turgid plant cell was placed in a concentrated solution of sucrose. The diagram shows the appearance of the cell after one hour:

(i) Label structures J and K. (2)

(ii) What evidence on the diagram shows that the water potential of the cell sap must be higher (less negative) than that of the sucrose solution? (1)

(iii) Use your knowledge of a property of structure K to explain why the water potential at T must be equal to that at S. (2)

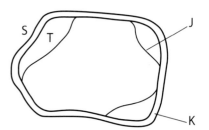

6 The diagram shows two plant cells X and Y as seen through a microscope. The figures show the solute potential ψ_s and the pressure potential ψ_p for both cells and the water potential ψ for cell Y.

Cell X

$\Psi_p = 1000\,kPa$
$\Psi_s = 1800\,kPa$

Cell Y

$\Psi_p = 0\,kPa$
$\Psi_s = 1000\,kPa$
$\Psi\ = 1000\,kPa$

Water relations in cells are given by the following equation: $\psi\ cell = \psi_s + \psi_p$

(a) Calculate the water potential of cell X. Show your working. (2)

(b) State the name of the condition shown by cell Y and explain how this condition could have arisen. (3)

(c) Suggest the effect on seedlings if all of their cells were in the condition as shown in cell Y. (1)

(d) What term is used to describe the process by which a cell loses water until its plasma membrane just draws away from its cell wall? (1)

(e) What would happen to an animal cell placed in a hypotonic solution? (1)

7 (a) Describe the structure of the cell membrane. (4)

(b) Describe the various ways in which small molecules enter the cell. (6)

BY1

Enzymes

In cells, metabolic reactions take place quickly and thousands of reactions are taking place simultaneously. Order and control is essential if reactions are not to interfere with each other. These features of metabolism are made possible by the action of enzymes.

By the end of this topic you should be able to:

- Describe the structure of enzymes and how their properties are related to their structure.
- Explain the mechanisms of action of enzyme molecules with reference to specificity, active site, enzyme–substrate complex.
- Explain how enzymes are affected by factors such as temperature, pH, and the concentration of the reactants.
- Explain how enzymes are affected by inhibitors.
- Explain the principle of immobilised enzymes and their advantages over 'free' enzymes.
- Describe the use of a biosensor to test for blood glucose.

YOU SHOULD KNOW ›››

››› the lock and key and induced fit models of enzyme action

››› how factors such as temperature, pH and substrate concentration affect the rate of an enzyme-catalysed reaction

How Science Works

Observation of enzyme molecules led scientists to propose the induced fit model of enzyme action.

▼ **Study points**

How could you carry out an experiment to determine the effect of temperature on the rate of breakdown of hydrogen peroxide by the enzyme, catalase?

If substrate becomes limiting, the addition of extra enzyme will not increase the rate of reaction.

Examiner tip
The curve is steepest at the start of the reaction. This is called the initial rate of reaction.

Models of enzyme action

Scientists often use a scientific model as a representation of how something works. The lock and key theory proposes that enzymes work in the same way as a key operates a lock. Each key has a specific shape that fits and operates a particular lock. In a similar way, a substrate will only fit the active site of one particular enzyme.

However, observations that the enzyme's shape was being altered by the binding molecule, suggest that the structure was flexible and not rigid as originally thought. Scientists then proposed an alternative model, called the induced fit model. This theory suggests that the enzyme has a certain general shape which alters slightly to accommodate the substrate. As the enzyme changes its shape it places a strain on the substrate molecule and distorts a particular bond. This lowers the activation energy needed to break the bond.

The course of an enzyme-controlled reaction

The progress of an enzyme-catalysed reaction for a fixed concentration of substrate can be followed by measuring either the formation of product or the disappearance of substrate.

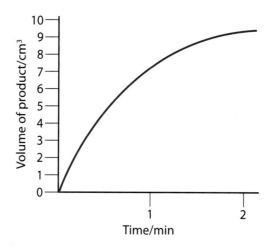

▲ Graph showing the measurement of formation of a product

The shape of the graph may be explained as follows:

- When the enzyme and substrate are first mixed together, there are a large number of substrate molecules.
- Both types of molecules are in constant motion.
- Substrate molecules come in contact with the empty active sites of the enzyme molecules.
- All active sites become filled with substrate molecules, which are rapidly broken down to product.
- As the reaction proceeds there is a decreasing amount of substrate and more and more product.
- In due course the graph flattens out because all the substrate has been used up and so no further product can be formed.

Factors affecting enzyme action

Enzymes are made inside living cells but may act inside the cell (intracellular) or outside (intercellular, extracellular) such as the digestive enzymes of the alimentary canal. Environmental conditions, such as temperature and pH, change the three-dimensional structure of enzyme molecules. Bonds are broken and hence the configuration of the active site is altered.

▼ **Study point**

Enzymes, rather than inorganic catalysts, are used widely in industry because they are more efficient. They have a higher turnover number and are very specific. They are also more economical as they work at lower temperatures.

The effect of temperature on rate of enzyme action

A rise in temperature increases the kinetic energy of molecules and they move around more quickly and collide with each other more often. In an enzyme-catalysed reaction, the enzyme and substrate molecules collide more often in a given time, increasing the rate of reaction. As a general rule, the rate of reaction doubles for each 10°C rise in temperature until an optimum temperature is reached. For most enzymes this is 40°C. Above this temperature the increasing vibration of the molecules causes the hydrogen bonds to break and cause a change in the tertiary structure of the enzyme. This alters the shape of the active site and the substrate will not fit into the active site. The enzyme is then said to be denatured. This is a permanent change in the structure. If enzymes are subjected to low temperatures, such as freezing, the enzyme is inactivated as the molecules have no kinetic energy. However, the enzyme can work again if the temperature is raised.

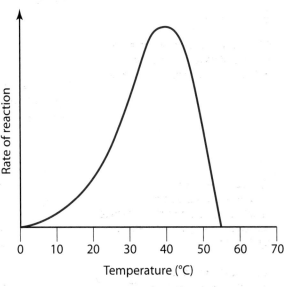

▶ *Effect of temperature on rate of reaction*

The effect of pH on rate of enzyme action

Most enzymes have an optimum pH at which the rate of reaction is at its maximum. Small changes in pH outside the optimum can cause small reversible changes in enzyme structure and result in inactivation. Extremes of pH can denature an enzyme.

The charges on the amino acid side-chains of the enzyme's active site are affected by free hydrogen ions or hydroxyl ions. In the formation of an enzyme substrate complex the charge on the active site must match those on the substrate. If the active site has too many H^+ ions (say) the active site and the substrate may both have the same charge and the enzyme will repel the substrate.

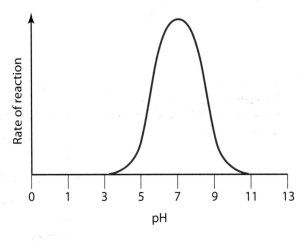

▶ *Effect of pH on rate of reaction*

▼ *How change in pH affects enzyme action*

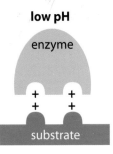

optimum pH

charges on active site match those of substrate so an enzyme–substrate complex forms

low pH

charges on active site repel substrate

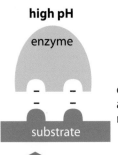

high pH

charges on active site repel substrate

At extremes of pH the hydrogen bonding is affected and the three-dimensional shape of the enzyme is altered and so is the shape of the active site.

Enzymes are also affected by the concentration of the substrate and the concentration of the enzyme itself.

Substrate concentration

The rate of an enzyme-catalysed reaction will vary with changes in substrate concentration. If the amount of enzyme is constant, the rate of reaction will increase as the substrate increases. At low substrate concentrations the enzyme molecules have only a limited number of substrate molecules to collide with. In other words, the active sites are not working to full capacity. As more substrate is added there must come a point when all the enzyme's active sites are filled. In other words, the rate of reaction is at a maximum.

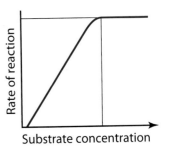

▶ *Effect of increasing substrate concentration*

▾ *Effect of low and high substrate concentration*

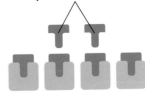

substrate molecules   empty active sites

only a limited number of substrate molecules to fill active sites

Low substrate concentration

excess substrate molecules unable to find any free active sites

the rate of reaction is at a maximum

High substrate concentration

Enzyme concentration

Once a product leaves the active site of an enzyme, that enzyme molecule can be reused. Therefore only a small concentration of enzyme is needed to catalyse a large number of substrate molecules. The number of substrate molecules that one molecule of enzyme can turn into products in one minute is called the turnover number. The enzyme, catalase, has a turnover number of several million.

The rate of an enzyme-catalysed reaction will vary with changes in enzyme concentration. Increasing the enzyme concentration will increase the number of available active sites and therefore the rate of reaction.

Enzyme inhibition

Inhibition occurs when enzyme action is slowed down or stopped by another substance. The inhibitor combines with the enzyme and either directly or indirectly prevents it forming an enzyme–substrate complex.

There are two types of inhibitors, competitive and non-competitive.

Competitive inhibition

Competitive inhibitors have a molecular shape similar to that of the substrate. This allows them to occupy the active site of an enzyme in place of the substrate. They therefore compete with the substrate for the active site. For example, malonic acid competes with succinate for the active sites of succinic dehydrogenase, an important enzyme in the Krebs cycle in respiration. If the substrate concentration is increased it will reduce the effect of the inhibitor. This is because the more substrate molecules present, the greater the chance of finding active sites, leaving fewer to be occupied by the inhibitor.

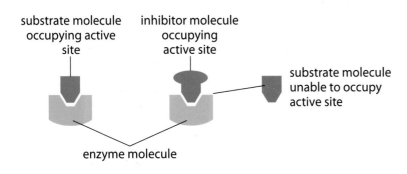

▲ *Competitive inhibition*

Non-competitive inhibition

Non-competitive inhibitors bind to the enzyme at a site which is not the active site. On attachment it alters the overall shape of the enzyme molecule, including the active site, in such a way that the active site can no longer accommodate the substrate. As the substrate and inhibitor molecules attach to different parts of the enzyme, they are not competing for the same sites. The rate of reaction is therefore unaffected by substrate concentration. For example, cyanide (a respiratory poison) attaches itself to part of the enzyme, cytochrome oxidase, and inhibits respiration.

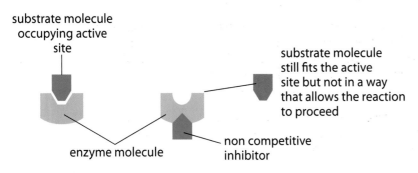

▲ *Non-competitive inhibition*

Examiner tip

Describe enzyme–substrate reactions in terms of molecular collisions. With competitive inhibition the greater the substrate concentration compared to the inhibitor, the greater the chance that the substrate will collide with the enzyme.

▼ **Study points**

The inhibitor is not permanently bound to the active site, thus, when it leaves, another molecule can take its place. This could be substrate or inhibitor, depending on the concentration of each present.

Do not be too concerned with the functions of malonic acid and cytochrome oxidase at this stage. These chemicals and their involvement in respiration are studied at A2.

11

Knowledge check

Identify the missing word or words.

Competitive inhibitors occupy the •••• •••• of an enzyme in place of the ••••. If the substrate concentration is ••••, it will reduce the effect of the inhibitor. •••• is an example of a non-competitive inhibitor which inhibits respiration.

Medical and industrial applications of enzymes

Immobilised enzymes

Immobilised enzymes are enzyme molecules that are fixed, bound or trapped on an inert matrix such as a gel capsule (alginate beads). These beads can be packed into glass columns. Substrate can be added to the top of the column and it reacts with the enzyme as it slowly flows down the column. Once set up the column can be used again and again. As the enzyme is fixed it does not get mixed up with the products and is therefore cheaper to separate. Immobilised enzymes are used widely in industrial processes, such as fermentation, as they can readily be recovered for reuse.

Examiner tip

Learn the definitions of terms. For example, can you define an immobilised enzyme?

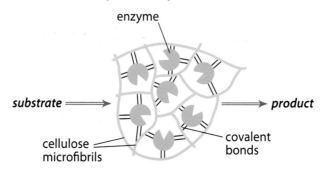

▲ Immobilised enzyme in framework of cellulose microfibrils

Enzyme instability is one of the key factors that prevent the wider use of 'free' enzymes. Chemicals such as organic solvents, raised temperatures and pH values outside the norm can denature the enzyme with a consequent loss of activity. Immobilising enzymes with a polymer matrix creates a microenvironment allowing reactions to occur at higher temperatures than normal. This means that activity is increased and so production is also increased. Other advantages include:

- Enzymes can tolerate a wider range of conditions.
- Enzymes are easily recovered for reuse thus reducing overall costs.
- Several enzymes with differing pH or temperature optima can be used together.
- Enzymes can be easily added or removed giving greater control over the reaction.

Examiner tip

Be prepared to compare the effect of temperature on a free and immobilised enzyme.

▶ *Graph showing the effect of temperature on the rate of reaction of the same enzyme in its free and in its immobilised state.*

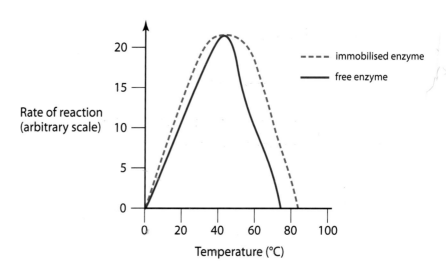

Biosensors

One use of immobilised enzymes involves **biosensors**, which work on the principle that enzymes are specific and are able to select one type of molecule from a mixture even in very low concentrations. A biosensor can be used in the rapid and accurate detection of minute traces of biologically important molecules.

Biosensors have great potential in the areas of medical diagnosis and environmental monitoring. The electrode probe can detect changes in substrate or product, temperature changes or optical properties.

One particular use of a biosensor is in the detection of blood sugar in diabetics. The electrode probe, which has a specific enzyme immobilised in a membrane, is placed in the blood sample. If glucose is present, it diffuses through the membrane, forming an enzyme–substrate complex. The reaction produces a small electric current, which is picked up by the electrode (the **transducer**).

This current is read by a meter which produces a reading for blood glucose. Normal blood glucose levels are described as being 3.89–5.83 mmol dm^{-3}.

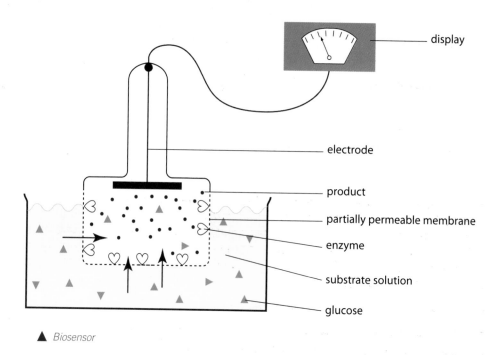

▲ *Biosensor*

Steps in using a biosensor

1. Blood contains a mixture of different molecules.
2. Enzyme electrode is placed in a blood sample.
3. Glucose diffuses into the immobilised enzyme layer.
4. Oxygen is taken up.
5. The rate of oxygen uptake is proportional to the glucose concentration.
6. A digital display shows an accurate concentration of glucose.

Key Term

Biosensor = the association of a biomolecule, such as an enzyme, with a **transducer**, which produces an electrical signal in response to substrate transformation. The strength of the electrical signal may be measured with a meter.

▼ Study point

Immobilised enzymes are also used in pregnancy testing kits and in a fermenter to provide a rapid, sensitive and specific measurement of products.

12 Knowledge check

Identify the missing word or words.

Enzymes that are fixed in a gel capsule are called .... enzymes. They are used in biosensors to detect .... in diabetics..

5 Milk can be made lactose-free by passing it down a column of the immobilised enzyme lactase. An experiment was carried out to determine the optimum size of alginate beads to use in this process. Three bead sizes were prepared and placed in columns. The same volume of milk was run into each column at the same rate of flow. The percentage of product for each experiment was determined. The experiment was repeated a number of times.

	Bead diameter (mm)		
	2	4	6
Mean percentage of product	98	84	70

(a)(i) Suggest the bead size that should be used in the process. Give a reason for your answer. (1)

(ii) Give two reasons for the different results from the three bead sizes. (2)

(iii) What result would be expected if the flow rate was decreased? Explain your answer. (1)

(iv) What other factor should be kept constant during the experiment? (1)

(b) Name the two monosaccharides produced by the breakdown of lactose. (1)

(c) State two advantages of using immobilised enzymes in industrial processes. (2)

6 The presence of glucose in a person's urine is an indication of diabetes. Glucose can be detected by placing a coloured plastic strip containing the immobilised enzyme, glucose oxidase, into a sample of urine. The strip changes colour if glucose is present.

(a) Explain why this diagnostic method is not suitable for the accurate measurement of the concentration of glucose in the urine. (2)

(b) Another method used to measure glucose involves the use of a biosensor.
The diagram shows an enzyme electrode from a glucose biosensor:

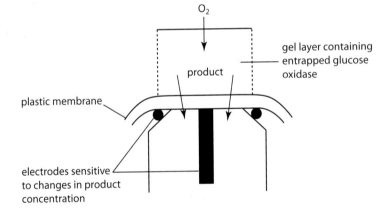

(i) Explain what is meant by the term *biosensor*. (2)

(ii) Describe the role of the enzyme. (2)

(iii) Describe how this biosensor can be used to measure blood glucose concentration. (4)

7 Describe the structure and function of enzymes. Explain how their activity is affected by pH, temperature and inhibitors. (10)

BY1

Nucleic acids and cell division

DNA is the molecule that contains the information about an organism in the form of a genetic code. This code determines inherited characteristics and is contained in the nucleus of each cell of that organism. The genetic code needs to be copied accurately over and over again, so that whenever the nucleus of a cell divides it can pass on an exact copy to the nuclei of the daughter cells. DNA performs two major functions: it replicates in dividing cells by the process called mitosis and it carries the information for the production of proteins.

By the end of this topic you should be able to:

- Describe the structure of nucleotides as sub-units of nucleic acids.
- Describe the structure of DNA.
- Compare the structure of DNA and RNA.
- Explain the need for the production of genetically identical cells in living organisms.
- Understand that the replication of DNA takes place during the interphase stage of mitosis.
- Describe the behaviour of chromosomes during mitosis and the formation of a spindle.
- Name the main stages of mitosis.
- Explain that as a result of mitosis, asexual reproduction can take place as well as the growth and repair of cells.
- Explain the significance of mitosis as a process in which the daughter cells are provided with identical copies of genes.
- Compare the significance of the differences between mitosis and meiosis.

Key Term

Homologous = chromosomes are in pairs, known as homologous pairs. One of each pair is derived from the chromosomes provided by the mother and the other is derived from chromosomes provided by the father.

▼ Study point

Knowledge of chromosome structure will help you to understand the process of mitosis.

Cell division

Inside the nucleus are chromosomes. Chromosomes contain DNA, which contains hereditary information that is transferred from cell to cell when cells divide. In any one species the number of chromosomes in each body cell remains constant. Mitosis is the division of the nucleus to produce two daughter nuclei containing identical sets of chromosomes.

Chromosome structure

Chromosomes are made up of DNA, protein and a small amount of RNA. DNA occurs as a single strand in the form of a double helix running the length of the chromosome. Each DNA molecule is made up of many sections called genes. It is only at the onset of cell division that chromosomes become visible. Shortly before cell division begins each DNA molecule makes a copy of itself. The single thread of DNA becomes two identical threads. These are called chromatids and they lie parallel along most of their length but are joined only in a specialised region called the centromere.

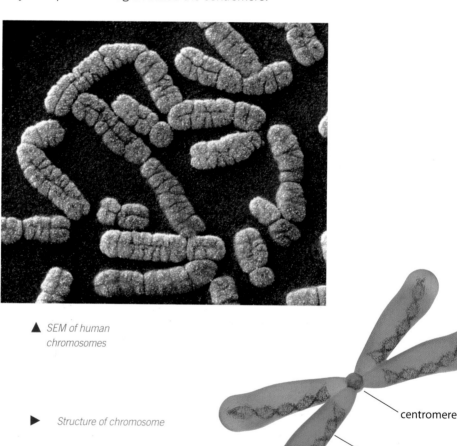

▲ SEM of human chromosomes

▶ Structure of chromosome

centromere

chromatid

Chromosome number

The number of chromosomes in the cells of different species varies. Humans always have 46 chromosomes, a fruit fly has 8 chromosomes, a potato 48 chromosomes! Chromosomes are found in matching pairs, called **homologous** pairs. So humans have 23 pairs of homologous chromosomes. The total number of chromosomes is called the diploid number. Sex cells, or gametes, have half the diploid number, this is called haploid. Human gametes have 23 chromosomes.

Mitosis

Mitosis produces two daughter cells that are genetically identical to the parent cell.

Dividing cells undergo a regular pattern of events known as the cell cycle. This is a continuous process but for convenience of description it is subdivided into four stages plus a 'resting' stage, known as interphase, between one complete division.

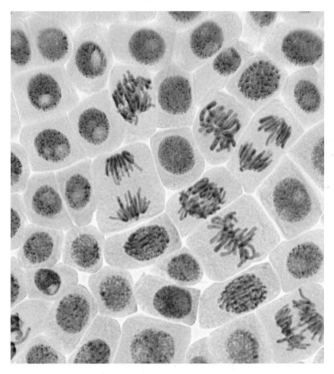

▲ *Micrograph of cells at various stages of mitosis*

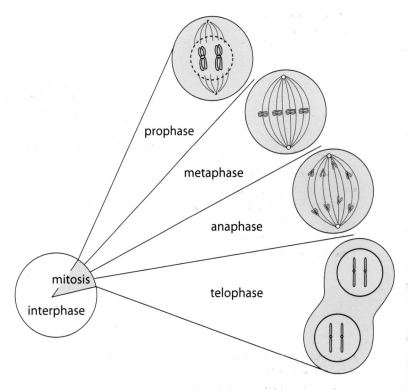

prophase

metaphase

anaphase

telophase

mitosis

interphase

▲ *Cell cycle*

Interphase

This is the longest part of the cycle during which a newly formed cell increases in size and produces organelles lost during the previous division. The quantity of DNA is doubled during this period. Just before the next cell division the chromosomes replicate so that each then consists of two chromatids joined together by the centromere. There is considerable metabolic activity as these processes need energy in the form of ATP. The chromosomes are not visible at interphase because the chromosome material, chromatin, is dispersed throughout the nucleus.

Prophase

This is the longest stage in mitosis.

During this stage the following changes take place:

- The chromosomes condense (shorten and become thicker) and become visible as long thin threads. They are now referred to as pairs of chromatids.

- Centrioles are present in animal cells; the centrioles divide and move to the opposite ends (poles) of the cells.

- Protein microtubules form from each centriole and the spindle develops, extending from pole to pole.

- Towards the end of prophase the nuclear membrane disintegrates and the nucleolus disappears.

- Pairs of chromatids can clearly be seen lying free in the cytoplasm.

Early prophase

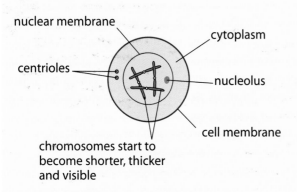

nuclear membrane

cytoplasm

centrioles

nucleolus

cell membrane

chromosomes start to become shorter, thicker and visible

Late prophase

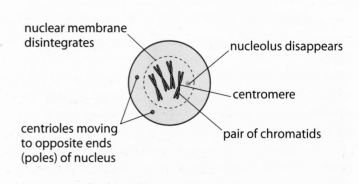

nuclear membrane disintegrates

nucleolus disappears

centromere

centrioles moving to opposite ends (poles) of nucleus

pair of chromatids

Metaphase

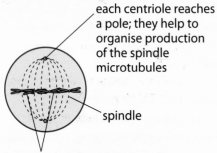

each centriole reaches a pole; they help to organise production of the spindle microtubules

spindle

chromosomes line up across the equator of the spindle attached by their centromeres to the spindle

Anaphase

chromatids move to opposite poles; centromeres first, pulled by the microtubules

Telophase

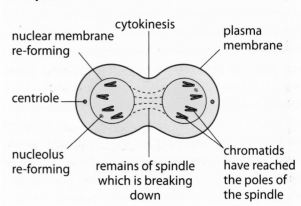

cytokinesis

plasma membrane

nuclear membrane re-forming

centriole

nucleolus re-forming

remains of spindle which is breaking down

chromatids have reached the poles of the spindle

▲ *Stages in mitosis*

Metaphase

During metaphase the chromosomes arrange themselves at the centre or equator of the spindle and become attached to certain spindle fibres at the centromere. Contraction of these fibres draws the individual chromatids slightly apart.

Anaphase

Anaphase is a very rapid stage. The centromere splits and the spindle fibres contract and pull the now separated chromatids to the poles, centromere first.

Telophase

This is the final stage of mitosis. The chromosomes have now reached the poles of the cells and are referred to as chromosomes again. They uncoil and lengthen. The spindle breaks down, the centrioles replicate, the nucleoli reappear and the nuclear membrane reforms. In animal cells cytokinesis occurs by the constriction of the centre of the parent cell from the outside inwards. In plant cells, a cell plate forms across the equator of the parent cell from the centre outwards and a new cell wall is laid down.

Significance of mitosis

- Mitosis produces two cells that have the same number of chromosomes as the parent cell and each chromosome is an exact replica of one of the originals. The division allows the production of cells that are genetically identical to the parent and so gives genetic stability.

- By producing new cells, mitosis leads to growth of an organism and also allows for repair of tissues and the replacement of dead cells. An example of mitosis in plants is in the root tip. In human skin, dead surface cells are replaced by identical cells from below.

- Asexual reproduction results in complete offspring that are identical to the parent. This takes place in unicellular organisms such as yeast, bacteria and some insects such as greenfly. It also takes place in certain flowering plants where organs such as bulbs, tubers and runners produce large numbers of identical offspring in a relatively short period of time. There is no variation between each individual. However, most of these plants also reproduce sexually.

REPRODUCTION, GROWTH & REPAIR ; TISSUE RENEWAL

Meiosis

In sexual reproduction two gametes fuse to form a zygote. For each generation to maintain a full set of chromosomes (diploid number) the chromosome number must be halved (haploid number) during meiosis.

Meiosis involves two divisions: meiosis I, where the chromosome number is halved; and meiosis II, where the two haploid nuclei divide again in a division identical to that of mitosis. The end result is the production of four daughter nuclei, each with half the number of chromosomes of the parent cell.

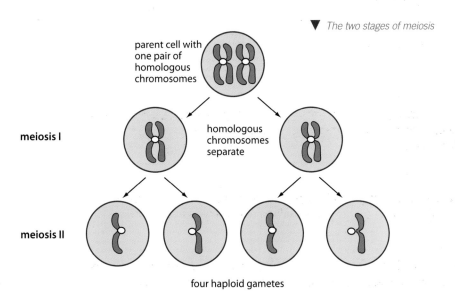

▼ *The two stages of meiosis*

parent cell with one pair of homologous chromosomes

meiosis I — homologous chromosomes separate

meiosis II

four haploid gametes

However, there is another important difference between meiosis and mitosis. During prophase I homologous chromatids wrap around each other and then partially repel each other but remain joined at certain points called chiasmata. At these points chromatids may break and recombine with a different but equivalent chromatid. This swapping of pieces of chromosomes is called crossing over and is a source of genetic variation.

During the first stage of metaphase of meiosis the pairs of homologous chromosomes arrange themselves randomly on the equator of the spindle. Only one of each pair passes into the daughter cell and this happens with each pair. Therefore the combination of chromosomes that goes into the daughter cell at meiosis I is also random. This random distribution and consequent independent assortment of chromosomes produces new genetic combinations.

Comparison of mitosis and meiosis

Mitosis	Meiosis
One division resulting in two daughter cells	Two divisions resulting in four daughter cells
Number of chromosomes is unchanged	Number of chromosomes is halved
Homologous chromosomes do not associate in pairs	Homologous chromosomes pair up
Crossing over does not occur	Crossing over occurs and chiasmata form
Daughter cells are genetically identical	Daughter cells are genetically different

Meiosis and variation

In the long term, if a species is to survive in a constantly changing environment and to colonise new environments, sources of variation are essential. There are three ways of creating variety:

- During sexual reproduction the genotype of one parent is mixed with that of the other when haploid gametes fuse.

- Independent assortment results in gametes containing different combinations of chromosomes.

- During crossing over equivalent parts of homologous chromosomes may be exchanged thus producing new combinations and the separation of linked genes.

▼ Comparison of stages of mitosis and meiosis

Metaphase of mitosis

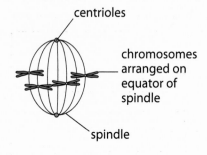

centrioles

chromosomes arranged on equator of spindle

spindle

Metaphase I of meiosis

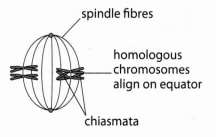

spindle fibres

homologous chromosomes align on equator

chiasmata

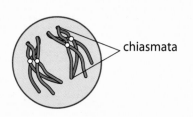

chiasmata

crossing over between some homologus chromosomes may occur

Nucleic acids and cell division

1   The diagram shows a section of a DNA molecule:

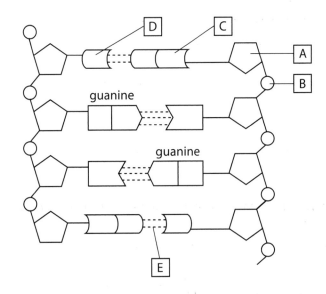

(a)   Name the parts labelled A and B. (2)

(b)   Name the type of bonding shown at E. (1)

(c)(i) What type of nitrogenous base is guanine? (1)

   (ii) Name the bases C and D. (2)

(d)   A large sample of DNA was analysed and found to contain 28% of the nitrogenous base guanine. Calculate the percentage of the molecule that would be thymine. (2)

2 (a)   Complete the table which compares DNA with messenger RNA (mRNA). (4)

Feature	DNA	mRNA
Name of sugar		
Number of carbon atoms in sugar		
Number of polynucleotide chains in molecule		
Location in cell		

(b)   The table below shows the relative amounts of the four bases in DNA taken from three sources:

	Nitrogenous base (relative amounts)			
Cellular source of DNA	Adenine	Guanine	Cytosine	Thymine
Rat muscle	28.6	21.4	21.5	28.4
Wheat seed	27.3	22.7	22.9	27.1
Yeast	31.3	18.7	17.1	32.9

   (i) Explain why the relative amount of adenine is almost the same as the relative amount of thymine in each source. (3)

  (ii) Explain why the base sequence of the DNA samples taken from the bone marrow of the rat would be the same as those taken from the muscle of the same rat. (3)

 (iii) Explain how the sample of DNA from the sperm of a rat differs from that of a muscle cell of the same rat. (3)

Biodiversity, evolution and classification

It is generally accepted that present-day organisms have arisen by gradual change from pre-existing forms of life over very long periods of time. The vast number of species that have evolved have been organised into manageable groups. Over the last 200 years certain human activities have had negative effects on the environment and this has, in turn, affected the survival of plants and animals. Extinction rates of species in certain areas such as the tropics have increased dramatically. Now scientists have come to realise that there is a biodiversity crisis, a rapid decrease in the variety of life on Earth.

Topic contents

By the end of this topic you should be able to:

- Define the terms: species, taxonomy, biodiversity, extinction and evolution.

- Understand that biodiversity has been generated through natural selection and adaptation over a long period of time.

- Describe adaptive radiation using Darwin's finches as an example.

- Describe the classification of species into the taxonomic hierarchy of kingdom, phylum, class, order, family, genus and species.

- Outline the binomial system of naming living organisms.

- Describe the characteristic features of the five kingdoms: Prokaryotae, Protoctista, Fungi, Plantae and Animalia.

- Describe the basic features of selected phyla.

- Outline how physical features and biochemical methods can be used to assess the relatedness of organisms.

Biodiversity

Human activities are altering ecosystems upon which they and other species depend. Tropical rain forests are being destroyed at an alarming rate to make room for, and to support, the increase in the human population. In the oceans, stocks of many fishes are being depleted by over-harvesting, and some of the most productive and diverse areas, such as coral reefs and estuaries, are being severely stressed. Globally, the rate of species loss may be as much as 50 times higher than at any time in the past 100,000 years. Human alteration to habitat is the single greatest threat to **biodiversity** on the planet.

Extinction is a natural process that has been taking place since life first evolved. It is the current *rate* of extinction that underlies the biodiversity crisis. Scientists believe that the normal 'background' rate of extinction is one out of every million species per year. It is now estimated that human activity, in tropical areas alone, has increased extinction rates between 1000 and 10,000 times! Massive destruction of habitats throughout the world has been brought about by agriculture, urban development, forestry, mining, and environmental pollution. Marine life has also been affected. About one-third of the planet's marine fish species rely on coral reefs. At the current rate of destruction about half of the reefs could be lost in the next 20 years.

The vast majority of Earth's earlier occupants, including the large and once dominant dinosaurs and tree ferns, have become extinct largely as a result of climatic, geological and biotic changes. At the present time, human activity has taken over as the main cause of species **evolution**. The main causes for the decline in numbers of larger mammals, such as mountain gorillas, giant pandas, tigers and polar bears are loss of habitat; over-hunting by humans; and competition from introduced species. Other species are also threatened by additional causes such as deforestation, pollution and drainage of wetlands.

It is now recognised that each species may represent an important human asset, a potential source of food, useful chemicals, or disease-resistant genes. For example, of the many plants growing in the tropical rain forests there may be some with medicinal properties. The extinction of any plant species before their chemical properties have been investigated could amount to an incalculable loss. There is therefore a need for species conservation, the planned preservation of wildlife.

Key Terms

Biodiversity = a measure of the number of species on the planet.

Extinction = the loss of species.

Evolution = the process by which new species are formed from pre-existing ones over very long periods of time.

Evolution

What has brought about the existence of so many different life-forms on Earth? The term evolution is used specifically for the processes that have transformed life on Earth from its early beginnings to the vast diversity of fossilised and living forms that are known today.

The theory of evolution was first proposed by Charles Darwin. In 1832, Charles Darwin, then aged 22, travelled to South America on the *HMS Beagle* to carry out a scientific survey. He studied the flora and fauna of mainland South America and of some surrounding islands, including the Galapagos Islands. These islands were formed in recent geological time, the result of volcanic activity. Consequently any life-forms present must have reached the islands from the mainland.

His task was to observe, describe and classify the plants and animals that he found. He also collected fossils in the rocks and these showed him that different life-forms had gone through many changes in the past. In 1859 he proposed natural selection as the force that causes changes in populations.

Darwin studied the fourteen different species of finches found on the Galapagos Islands. Finches are unable to fly long distances, and since the mainland is 600 miles distant, Darwin suggested that one ancestral species of finch had reached the islands with the help of the prevailing winds. As there were no other bird species inhabiting the islands,

▼ Study point

You are not required to study Darwin's theory of natural selection. This is encountered at A2.

there was a variety of food available to the colonising finches. He noticed how individual finches differed from one island to the next. The main differences were in the size and shape of their beaks and these were related to the different type of food eaten, for example insects, seeds, fruit.

Insect-eaters

warbler finch

Seed-eaters

vegetarian tree finch

Mainly insect-eaters – but seeds also eaten

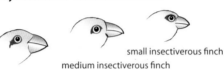

small insectiverous finch

medium insectiverous finch

large insectiverous finch

Mainly seed-eaters – but insects also eaten

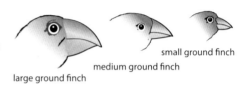

small ground finch

medium ground finch

large ground finch

▲ *Different types of finch beaks*

It seemed that on each island the characteristics that best suited a particular finch to its environment were inherited by the offspring. Darwin suggested that the finches had developed from a common ancestor and that the type of beak had developed over time and become specialised to feed on a particular food source. This is an example of **adaptive radiation**.

Taxonomy

It is believed that there are between 3 and 30 million species of living organisms on Earth but, to date, only about two million different kinds of organisms have been described and identified. The sorting of living organisms into groups of a manageable size is known as **taxonomy** or classification.

When describing plants and animals taxonomists look for differences and similarities between them and place similar organisms closely together and dissimilar ones further apart. A classification system based on large groups being divided up into progressively smaller groups is said to be hierarchical.

The natural classification used today was devised by the Swedish scientist, Linnaeus, in the 18th century. In this scheme, organisms are grouped together according to their basic similarities. A **hierarchical** system has been devised to distinguish large groups of organisms with a series of rank names to identify the different levels within the hierarchy:

- Kingdom – the largest taxonomic grouping, e.g. animals, plants.

- Phylum – a large grouping of all the classes that share some common features, e.g. Arthropods (includes insects, spiders, centipedes and millipedes, crustaceans).

- Class – a grouping of similar orders, e.g. Insecta (insects).

- Order – grouping of related families, e.g. Orthoptera (includes locusts, grasshoppers and crickets).

- Family – a grouping of similar genera (plural of genus), e.g. Rosaceae (rose)

- Genus – a group of species that are very closely related. For example, *Locusta*.

- Species – a group of organisms which share a large number of common characteristics and which can interbreed to produce fertile offspring. For example *Locusta migratoria*.

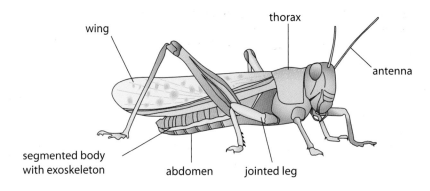

▲ *Diagram of locust*

Moving up the hierarchy from **species** to kingdom means that the relationship between organisms in the groups decreases. Moving down the hierarchy from kingdom to species means that the organisms are more closely related.

Phylogeny

The hierarchical order of taxonomic ranks is based on the evolutionary line of descent of the members of the group. The **phylogenetic** relationships of different species are usually represented by a tree-like diagram called a phylogenetic tree. In these diagrams the oldest species is at the base of the tree while more recent ones are represented by the ends of the branches.

Link You should know about the principles of modern classification that show how organisms may be related through evolution by the number of common characteristics they share. Refer to page 72.

Examiner tip
Be prepared to place taxa in the correct order.

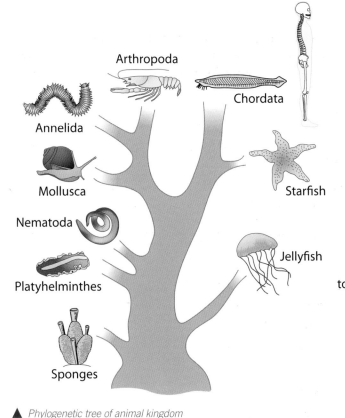

▲ *Phylogenetic tree of animal kingdom*

▼ *Phylogenetic tree of chordates*

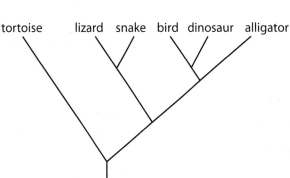

Binomial system

Many living organisms have common names, which may differ from one country to another. This can be confusing and even more confusing if a particular species needs to be named and described in a scientific research paper, which may be read by a scientist from a different country.

To overcome the problem, organisms are named according to the binomial system. This system was introduced by Linnaeus in 1753 and is based on using Latin as an international language. Each organism is given two names, the name of its genus and the name of its species. This system means that an organism is given precise identification worldwide, whereas the common name is not. The binomial system is still successfully used today because not only does each particular organism have its own unique scientific name but it also allows biologists to recognise that two species are closely related, e.g. *Panthera leo* (lion) and *Panthera tigris* (tiger).

When using the binomial system certain rules must be followed:

- The genus name is the first word and always has a capital letter.
- The species name always comes second and does not have a capital letter.
- The first time the scientific name is used in a text it should be written out in full. For example, *Panthera tigris*
- In any following text the genus name may then be abbreviated, *P. tigris*.
- Both names should be printed in italics, or underlined when written.

▼ **Study point**

The closer the branches, the closer the evolutionary relationship.

▼ **Study point**

Note that the genus name is given a capital letter and the species name is in lower case.

Both are in italics.

▼ **Study point**

You should learn the basic features which distinguish the five kingdoms.

The five kingdom classification

Living organisms are divided into five large groups or kingdoms.

Prokaryotae

These are unicellular organisms including bacteria and blue-green algae. They have no internal cell membranes, no nuclear membrane, no endoplasmic reticulum, no mitochondria and no Golgi body. They possess a cell wall but it is not made of cellulose.

▼ *Bacteria*

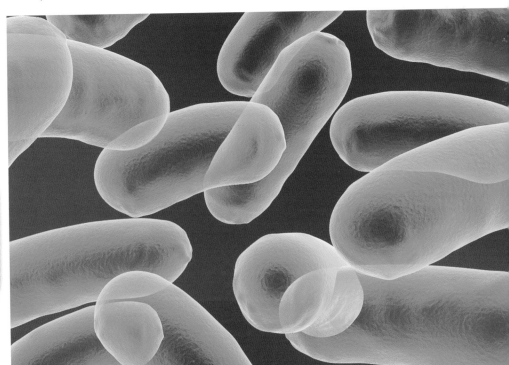

16

Knowledge check

Place the following taxa in order of size starting with the largest group and ending with the smallest group: order, genus, phylum, class, kingdom, family.

Protoctista

These are mostly small eukaryotic organisms, with membrane-bound organelles and a nucleus, with a nuclear membrane. In this kingdom are found the organisms that are not plants or animals or fungi. The kingdom includes algae, the water moulds, the slime moulds and the protozoa.

▼ *Euglena*

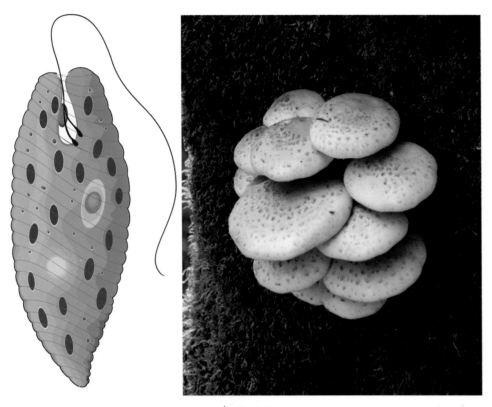

▲ *Bracket fungus*

▼ Study point

The Protoctista is sometimes referred to as 'the ragbag kingdom' as it contains all the organisms that cannot be fitted into any of the other kingdoms.

Link The flowering plants (Angiosperms) are the most dominant plant group on Earth. They include all our major crops and are therefore an important food source. Their flowers have seeds that are enclosed in a fruit formed from the ovary wall. Plant reproduction is studied in detail at A2 level.

Fungi

Eukaryotic, the body consisting of a network of threads called hyphae, forming a mycelium. There is a rigid cell wall made of chitin. They do not have photosynthetic pigments, and feeding is heterotrophic; all members of the group are either saprophytic or parasitic. In some subgroups, the hyphae have no cross-walls, but in others cross-walls, or septa, are present. Reproduction is by spores that lack flagella. Examples are *Penicillium*, yeast, mushroom.

Plants

These are multicellular and carry out photosynthesis. The cells are eukaryotic, have cellulose walls, vacuoles containing cell sap, and chloroplasts containing photosynthetic pigments.

The main plant phyla include mosses and liverworts, ferns, conifers and flowering plants.

Animals

These are multicellular, heterotrophic, eukaryotes, with cells lacking a cell wall and show nervous co-ordination.

Knowledge check

17

Match the following four kingdoms with features A–D.

1. Fungi.

2. Plants.

3. Animals.

4. Prokaryotae.

A. Unicellular, no nuclear membrane.

B. Cellulose cell walls and chloroplasts.

C. Cell wall made of chitin, possess hyphae.

D. Lack a cell wall, possess nervous co-ordination.

▾ **Study point**

95% of all animals are invertebrates and only 5% are vertebrates.

▲ *Lobster*

18

Knowledge check

Identify the missing word or words.

Arthropod features include an exoskeleton and ••••. The exoskeleton consists of a thick cuticle made of ••••. It provides support but is fixed in size and so the arthropod has to periodically shed its skin by a process called ••••.

Selected phyla from the animal kingdom

Animal biodiversity is classified into over twenty major phyla and several minor ones. Each phylum contains organisms based on a basic blueprint.

To illustrate this, three animal phyla have been selected, Annelida, Arthropoda and Chordata. They have been chosen for study as they are encountered in gaseous exchange, the circulation system and reproduction later in this unit.

The animal kingdom is divided into two main groups:

- Non-chordates, often called invertebrates. Examples include segmented worms, molluscs and arthropods.

- Chordates – all but the simplest of the chordates have a vertebral column and are therefore referred to as vertebrates and include fish, amphibians, reptiles, birds and mammals.

Annelida

There are 8,000 named species of annelids. They include earthworms, leeches and lugworms. All members of the phylum have the following common features:

- A long, thin segmented body, the segments being visible externally as rings with a body divided internally by partitions (septa).

- A fluid-filled body cavity (haemocoel).

- A hydrostatic skeleton.

- A head end with a primitive brain and a nervous system running the length of the body.

- A thin permeable skin, through which gaseous exchange occurs.

- A closed circulatory system containing an oxygen-carrying pigment.

Arthropoda

The arthropods are the most numerous and most successful of all the animal phyla. They have the following features in common:

- A body divided into segments.

- A well-developed brain.

- An open circulatory system and a cavity which surrounds the body organs.

- A hard outer exoskeleton.

- Paired jointed legs.

Two important evolutionary developments of this phylum are:

- Jointed legs modified to perform a variety of functions including: walking, swimming, jumping, feeding, reproduction.

- Exoskeleton – the outermost layer of cells of the body secretes a thick cuticle, which consists mainly of chitin. This performs several functions:

  – Protection of internal organs, protection from predators.

  – A point of attachment for muscles.

  – Support – for small animals a hollow tubular structure surrounding the body provides greater support than a solid cylindrical rod within it (an endoskeleton as in vertebrates) made from the same quantity of material.

  – In most terrestrial arthropods the exoskeleton is covered with a layer of wax, which reduces water loss.

The one main disadvantage of the exoskeleton is that it is fixed in size and does not grow with the animal. This contrasts with the vertebrate endoskeleton which increases in size as the body grows. In order to grow, an arthropod must periodically shed its **exoskeleton** (ecdysis). This leaves the animal especially vulnerable as the new exoskeleton hardens. The phylum Arthropoda is divided into four classes:

- Myriopoda – they have many pairs of legs, one or two per segment, examples are millipedes and centipedes.

- Crustacea – have between 10 and 20 pairs of legs, e.g. crab.

- Spiders – have four pairs of legs.

- Insects – have three pairs of legs.

It is an incredible fact that 75% of all animals are insects! They are by far the most successful group of animals on Earth. In many ways they are more successful than humans.

Insects occupy most habitats and have also conquered the air.

▲ *Beetle*

Insects belong to the Arthropod phylum but are split off into the class Insecta because the adult insects have the following features not found in other Arthropods:

- They have three pairs of legs, one pair to each of the segments of the thorax.

- The head has a pair of antennae and compound eyes.

- Gas exchange is by gills in aquatic insects and tracheae in terrestrial forms.

- Many insect species have evolved wings, making them the only invertebrates that can fly. They are powerful flying machines and it is this power of flight that has played a large part in their success.

The presence in the adult of two pairs of wings and six legs is a diagnostic feature of insects. In the evolution of some insect groups these features may have been secondarily lost. This has happened in the evolution of fleas and lice.

▼ **Study point**

Note the progression from water to land in the vertebrate classes. Different terrestrial groups have adapted to life on land in different ways. The evolution from aquatic to a terrestrial existence will be studied in more detail later in the unit.

▼ **Study point**

You should have an overview of a variety of organisms and their comparative adaptations. You are not expected to memorise the detailed classification of any of the groups.

Chordata

There are 60,000 named species of **Chordates**. Examples include frogs, snakes, eagles and humans. Vertebrates possess:

- A vertebral column or backbone.

- A well-developed brain, enclosed in a cranium.

The vertebrates are subdivided into five classes:

- Fish – aquatic forms with scales, fins and gills.

- Amphibians – these were the first land vertebrates, partly terrestrial and partly aquatic. They have a soft, moist skin. The eggs are fertilised externally in water where they also develop. Young (larvae) are aquatic and have gills, adults are usually terrestrial and have simple lungs.

- Reptiles – mainly terrestrial and have a dry skin with scales. They have lungs. The eggs are fertilised internally, covered with a shell and laid on land.

- Birds – similar to reptiles in many ways. Differences are mainly due to the ability to fly and the development of feathers, with fore-legs developed as wings. They have lungs. Eggs have hard shells.

- Mammals – skin with hair. Young are born alive and are fed on milk. Have lungs. They are further subdivided into two groups:

  – Marsupials, e.g. kangaroo – young are born at a very immature state and develop in female's pouch.

  – Placentals – young undergo considerable development in the mother's womb, and receive nourishment via the placenta before they are born.

◀ *Dolphin*　　　▲ *Lion*　　　▲ *Koala*

Evidence of common ancestry

So far you have learnt that taxonomy is the study of grouping or classifying organisms and is concerned with:

- Discovering and describing biological diversity.

- Investigating evolutionary relationships between organisms.

- Classifying these organisms so as to reflect these relationships.

The theory of evolution suggests that widely separated groups of organisms share a common ancestor. Therefore it would be expected that they share certain basic structural features. How similar they are should indicate how closely related they are in terms of evolution. Groups with little in common are assumed to have diverged from a common ancestor much earlier in geological history than groups which have a lot in common.

Using physical features

In deciding how closely related two organisms are a biologist needs to look for structures that, though they may serve quite different functions, are similar, suggesting a common origin. Such structures are said to be **homologous**. A good example of this is the **pentadactyl** limb of Chordata (vertebrates), which is found in the four classes of terrestrial vertebrates, amphibians, reptiles, birds and mammals. The structure of the limb is basically the same in all the classes. However, the limbs of the different vertebrates have become adapted for different functions, such as grasping, walking, swimming and flying, in a selection of vertebrates.

Examples of the pentadactyl limb modified for different functions are the human arm, the wing of a bat, the flipper of a whale, the wing of a bird, the leg of a horse.

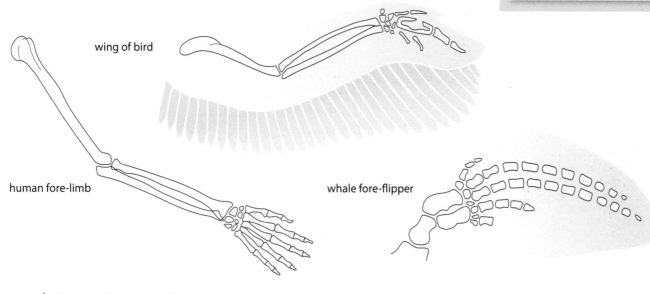

wing of bird

human fore-limb

whale fore-flipper

▲ *Pentadactyl limb of three different vertebrates*

Using information such as this it is possible to construct evolutionary trees where the end products of evolution have certain structural features in common with each other and with the ancestral stock from which they arise. The more similar two organisms are the more recently they are assumed to have diverged.

However, there is a possible danger in assuming that just because two animals look similar that they are related. Consider a shark, a porpoise and a penguin.

Key Term

Homologous = having a common origin but serve a different function.

Pentadactyl = having five digits.

Analogous = having the same function but a different origin.

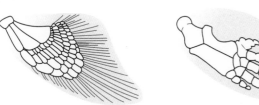

shark, a cartilaginous fish

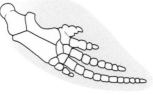

dolphin, an aquatic mammal

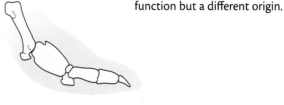

penguin, an aquatic bird no longer able to fly

▲ *Convergent evolution*

One is a fish, one is a bird and the other is a mammal. By studying the skeleton of the fore-limbs it is possible to deduce that the dolphin and the penguin have modified pentadactyl limbs, but the fish does not. The shark and dolphin are animals that have similar fore-limbs because they live in similar environments and have become adapted to that environment, not because they have a common ancestor. That is, the structures, limbs, are performing the same function. Such structures are described as **analogous**. Another example is the wings of birds and insects.

Using genetic evidence

During the course of evolution, when one species gives rise to another, the new species will have some differences in the sequence of nucleotide bases in the DNA. Over time the new species will accumulate more differences in the DNA. Therefore one would expect species that are more closely related to show more similarity in their DNA base sequences than species that are more distantly related.

DNA analysis has been used to confirm evolutionary relationships and can reduce the mistakes made in classification due to **convergent evolution**.

The technique of DNA hybridisation involves the extraction and comparison of the DNA of two species. The sequence of bases is compared and the more alike the sequences, the closer the organisms are related in terms of evolution.

The sequence of amino acids in proteins is determined by DNA. Therefore the degree of similarity in the amino acid sequence of the same protein in two species will reflect how closely related the two species are. Part of the fibrinogen molecule of various mammals has been compared and the sequence has been found to differ in varying degrees from one species to another and this has enabled scientists to draw up a possible evolutionary tree for mammals.

The proteins of different species can also be compared using immunological techniques. The principle behind this involves the fact that antibodies of one species will respond to specific antigens on proteins, such as albumin, in the blood serum of another. When antibodies respond to corresponding antigens a precipitate is formed. The greater the degree of precipitation the closer the evolutionary relationship.

Key Term

Convergent evolution = the tendency of unrelated organisms to acquire similar structures.

19

Knowledge check

Match the definitions 1–4 with the terms A–D.

1. Homologous.

2. Analogous.

3. Convergent evolution.

4. DNA analysis.

A. A method of comparing the DNA of two species.

B. The tendency of unrelated organisms to acquire similar structures.

C. Having a common origin but a different function.

D. Having the same function but a different origin.

How Science Works

One aspect of evolution that has been a mystery until recently is that of human evolution. As new techniques are developed our knowledge of primate evolution has been revised. Different techniques have provided conflicting evidence for the relationships between different primates. This illustrates the need to use a variety of evidence from different sources in making valid scientific conclusions.

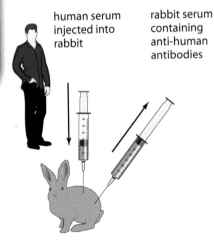

human serum injected into rabbit

rabbit serum containing anti-human antibodies

rabbit serum added to other species

dog   spider monkey   baboon   chimpanzee   human

precipitate

increasing amount of precipitation showing a closer evolutionary relationship

▲ *Immunological comparisons of human serum with that of other species*

To work out how closely related two species of primates are, such as humans and chimpanzees, the DNA strands from both species are extracted, separated and cut into fragments. The fragments from the two species are then mixed and analysed. This technique gives results which show that chimpanzees and humans have 97.6% DNA in common, whereas humans and rhesus monkeys have 91.1% DNA in common. Recent studies using this technique have also shown that the hippopotamus and whale are closely related.

Biodiversity, evolution and classification

1   State the term for each of the following (5):

(a)   A group of organisms which can interbreed to produce fertile offspring.

(b)   The process by which new species are formed from pre-existing ones over long periods of time.

(c)   A measure of the number of species on the planet.

(d)   The system whereby each organism is given two names, the name of its genus and the name of its species.

(e)   The scientific study of the diversity of living organisms.

2   The table lists five organisms, together with the five kingdoms. Tick a box to place each organism in the kingdom to which it belongs. (5)

	Plantae	Animalia	Protoctista	Fungi	Prokaryotae
Jellyfish					
Yeast					
Amoeba					
Fern					
Bacterium					

3 (a)   Complete the table which shows the classification of some organisms, including two features only of the phylum where applicable. (9)

Kingdom	Phylum	Features of phylum	Class	Example
Animalia	Annelida	1. 2.	Polychaeta	Lugworm *Arenicola marina*
Animalia		Soft moist skin Aquatic larva with gills; Adults with simple lungs		Common frog *Rana temporaria*
Animalia		1. 2.		Desert locust *Schistocerca gregaria*
	Basidiomycota	Hyphae; cell wall of chitin; reproduce using spores.	Basiiomyctes	Field mushroom *Agaricus campestris*

(b)   Name the genus of the Desert locust. (1)

4 The sequence of amino acids in the haemoglobin molecules of three species has been used to determine their evolutionary relationships. The results show the same sections of the haemoglobin molecules of the three mammals, each letter represents one amino acid:

Macroderma gigas	---GEEKAAVTGLWGKVNVE------DS -------S
Phoca vitulina	---GEEKSAVTALWGKVNVD------DS---------S
Balaenoptera acutorostrata	---AEEKSAVTALWAKVNVE------EA ---------T

(a) There are 7 differences between *B. acutorostrata* and *M. gigas*.

There are 3 differences between *P. vitulina* and *M. gigas*.

How many differences are there between *P. vitulina* and *B. acutorostrata*? (1)

(b) Which species is more closely related to *P. vitulina*? (1)

---

5 (a) The Galapagos finches illustrate the evolution of different birds from one ancestral form. What term is given to this evolutionary spread of new forms? (1)

(b) If a new species of finch was introduced into Britain today, it would be extremely unlikely for it to give rise to a similar variety of descendants to those on the Galapagos Islands. What is the difference between the situation today and the situation when the first finches arrived on the Galapagos? (2)

(c) Why are the finches of the Galapagos now recognised as a separate species, rather than a variety of the same species? (1)

---

6 20,000 years ago cheetahs (*Acinonyx jubatus*) roamed throughout the savannahs and plains of the four continents of Africa, Asia, Europe and North America. About 10,000 years ago, due to climate change, all but one species of the cheetah became extinct. With the drastic reduction in their numbers, close relatives were forced to breed, with the result that the cheetah became genetically inbred. This means that all present-day cheetahs are closely related.

(a) Classify the cheetah into phylum, class and genus. (3)

(b) Name one feature in each case that identifies a cheetah correctly into its phylum and class. (2)

(c)(i) Name a biochemical method could have been used to determine that all cheetahs are closely related. (1)

(ii) Briefly describe the results expected. (1)

---

7 The animals in the diagram belong to the phylum Arthropoda.

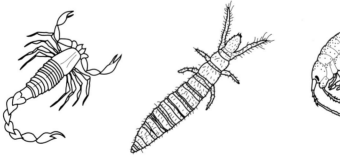

(a) Apart from having an exoskeleton, name two other features that you can see in the diagram that members of the Arthropoda have in common. (2)

(b) Give one advantage and one disadvantage of an exoskeleton. (2)

(c) Each of the animals above belongs to one of the four main sub-groups of the Arthropoda. Name the taxonomic level of these sub-groups. (1)

BY2

Adaptions for gaseous exchange

All living organisms exchange gases with the environment. They need oxygen to convert organic molecules, such as glucose, into energy by the process of respiration. In turn, waste gases have to be removed.

Organisms live in different environments; some live in water and others on land. An aquatic environment is fairly constant but life on land can be more extreme, ranging from the rarefied atmosphere at the top of a mountain, to the intense heat of the arid desert. In order to survive, living organisms have adapted in different ways.

By the end of this topic you should be able to describe:

- How unicellular organisms exchange gases through the body surface by diffusion.
- How simple multicellular organisms have adapted for gaseous exchange to allow an increase in body size.
- The specialised respiratory surfaces of larger multicellular organisms, including gills in fish, lungs in mammals and tracheae in insects.
- The ventilation mechanisms that have evolved in the fish and human in order to maintain gradients across respiratory surfaces.
- The structure and functions of the human respiratory system.
- The distribution of alveoli and blood vessels in lung tissue.
- The adaptations of chordate groups and insects to gaseous exchange on land.
- The leaf as an organ of gaseous exchange in plants.
- The structure and role of the various parts of a leaf.
- The opening and closing mechanism of stomata.

YOU SHOULD KNOW ›››

››› the structure of a fish gill

››› the difference between counter-current and parallel flow

››› the advantage of counter-current flow

››› the ventilation mechanism for forcing water over the gill filaments

▼ Study point

The various respiratory surfaces need a means of ventilation to supply them with a fresh supply of oxygen and to maintain diffusion gradients. That is, the function of a ventilation mechanism is to move the respiratory medium, air or water, over the respiratory surface.

Examiner tip

Be prepared to draw arrows on given diagrams to indicate the direction of blood flow and water flow.

Gas exchange in fish

Aquatic organisms have a problem with gaseous exchange because water contains far less oxygen than air and the rate of diffusion in water is slower. Also, water is a dense medium compared to air and does not flow as freely. As fish are very active they need a good supply of oxygen. In fish, gaseous exchange takes place across a special surface, the gill, over which a one-way current of water is kept flowing by a specialised pumping mechanism. The density of the water prevents the gills from collapsing and laying on top of each other, which would reduce the surface area. Gills are made up of many folds, providing a large surface area over which water can flow, and gases can be exchanged.

Fish are divided into two main groups according to the material that makes up their skeleton:

- Cartilaginous fish, e.g. sharks, have a skeleton made entirely of cartilage. Nearly all live in the sea. Just behind the head on each side are five gill clefts which open at gill slits. Water is taken into the mouth and is forced through the gill slits when the floor of the mouth is raised. Blood travels through the gill capillaries in the same direction as the sea water. Gas exchange in such a parallel flow is relatively inefficient.

- Bony fish have an internal skeleton made of bone and the gills are covered with a flap called the operculum. Bony fish inhabit both fresh and sea water and are by far the most numerous of aquatic vertebrates. Gas exchange involves a counter-current flow arrangement whereby blood in the gill capillaries flows in the opposite direction to the water flowing over the gill surface.

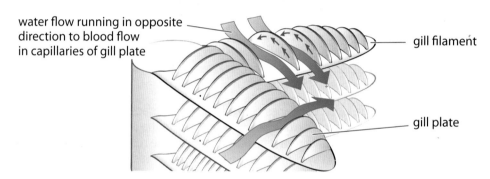

water flow running in opposite direction to blood flow in capillaries of gill plate

gill filament

gill plate

▲ *Gill plate*

In bony fish there are four pairs of gills in the pharynx and each gill is supported by a gill arch. Along each gill arch are many thin plates called gill lamellae and on these are the gas exchange surfaces, the gill plates. Out of water the gill collapses as the gill lamellae lie on top of each other and stick together. However, in water they are supported and provide a large surface area. The gill plates contain blood capillaries and the oxygen passes through the gill plates into the capillaries and carbon dioxide passes out into the water.

Gills provide:

- A specialised area rather than using the whole body surface.

- A large surface extended by the gill filaments.

- An extensive network of blood capillaries to allow efficient diffusion and haemoglobin for oxygen carriage.

To increase efficiency water needs to be forced over the gill filaments by pressure differences so maintaining a continuous, unidirectional flow of water. A lower pressure is maintained in the opercular cavity than in the bucco-pharynx. The **operculum** acts as both a valve, permitting water out, and as a pump drawing water past the gill filaments. The mouth also acts as a pump.

The ventilation mechanism for forcing water over the gill filaments operates as follows:

- The mouth opens.
- The operculum closes.
- The floor of the mouth is lowered.
- The volume inside the mouth cavity increases.
- The pressure inside the cavity decreases.
- Water flows in as the external pressure is higher than the pressure inside the mouth.
- These processs are reversed to force the water out over the gill filaments.

Key Term

Operculum = gill cover.

Inspiration = breathing in.

Expiration = breathing out.

21 Knowledge check

Identify the missing word or words.

In the gills of a cartilaginous fish a parallel flow system operates. In a bony fish a •••• flow system is found. In the latter the water flows in the opposite direction to the •••• flow. This •••• the efficiency of gas exchange because the •••• ••••• is maintained over the whole length of the •••• •••••.

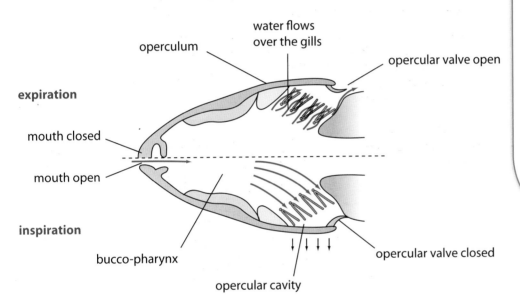

▲ *Ventilation of gills*

Counter-current flow

The orientation of the gas exchange surfaces is such that as the water passes from the pharynx into the opercular chamber, it flows between the gill plates in the opposite direction to the blood flow. This increases efficiency of gas exchange because the diffusion gradient between the adjacent flows is maintained over the whole length of the gill filament. That is, the blood always meets water with relatively higher oxygen content. This system allows the gills of a bony fish to remove 80% of the oxygen from water. This is three times the rate of extraction of oxygen from air in human lungs. This high level of extraction is essential to fish as there is around 25 times less oxygen in water, compared with air.

The counter-current system maintains a diffusion gradient along the whole length of the gill plate.

▶ *Counter-current system*

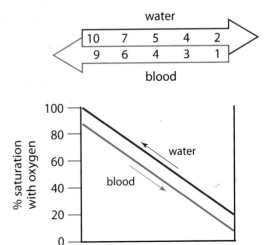

in counter-current flow a higher blood oxygen concentration can be reached than with parallel flow

Key Term

Terrestrial organism = an organism that lives on land.

Adaptations of vertebrate groups to gaseous exchange

The problem for all **terrestrial organisms** is that water evaporates from the body surface resulting in dehydration. Gas exchange surfaces need to be thin, permeable surfaces with a large area. These features conflict with the need to conserve water. Vertebrates and insects have evolved different methods of overcoming this problem.

Life is thought to have evolved in water, with animals adapting in order to colonise the land and some becoming highly modified for flight. Gills do not function out of water and there was a need for vertebrates to evolve a different form of gaseous exchange surface, the lung. Birds and mammals are particularly active and adapted for exchange with air, a less dense medium, instead of water, so have internal lungs to minimise loss of water and heat.

Amphibians

The amphibians include frogs, toads and newts. In the frog, gaseous exchange takes place through the skin and in the lungs. When inactive, the skin alone acts as the surface of gaseous exchange with either water or air. The skin is moist and permeable, with a well-developed capillary network just below the surface. The lungs are simple elastic sacs with a good blood supply. There is no diaphragm or rib cage and the lungs are inflated by forcing air into them by movements of the floor of the mouth.

Reptiles

Reptiles include crocodiles, lizards, and snakes. The few present-day reptiles are descendants of a once very successful group of animals, including the dinosaurs, which dominated the Earth about 200 million years ago. They are far better suited to life on land than amphibians. Reptiles can move on all four limbs without the trunk of the body touching the ground. Pairs of ribs project from the vertebrae (backbone). Ribs provide support and protection to the organs in the body cavity. Ribs are also involved in the ventilation of the lungs. The lung also has a more complex internal structure than that of amphibians with the in-growth of tissues increasing the surface area for gas exchange.

Birds

The lungs of birds have an internal structure similar to that of mammals. However, large volumes of oxygen are needed to provide the energy for flight. Ventilation of the lungs in birds is far more efficient than in other vertebrates and is assisted by a system of air sacs, which function as bellows. Ventilation of the lungs is brought about by the movement of the ribs. During flight the action of the flight muscles ventilates the lungs.

Gaseous exchange in insects

Most insects are terrestrial. In common with all terrestrial organisms, water evaporates from the body surface with the result that dehydration may occur. Efficient gas exchange requires a thin, permeable surface with a large area, which conflicts with the need to conserve water.

To reduce water loss, terrestrial organisms need to have waterproof coverings over their body surfaces. To overcome this problem insects have evolved a rigid exoskeleton which is covered by a cuticle. Insects have a relatively small surface area to volume ratio and so cannot use their body surface to exchange gases by diffusion.

Instead they have evolved a different system of gaseous exchange to other land animals. Gas exchange occurs through paired holes, called spiracles, running along the side of the body. The spiracles lead into a system of branched chitin lined air-tubes called tracheae. The spiracles can open and close like valves. This allows gaseous exchange to take place and also reduces water loss.

Resting insects rely on diffusion to take in oxygen and to remove carbon dioxide. During periods of activity, such as during flight, movements of the abdomen ventilate the tracheae. The ends of the tracheal branches are called tracheoles; here gaseous exchange takes place resulting in oxygen passing directly into the cells.

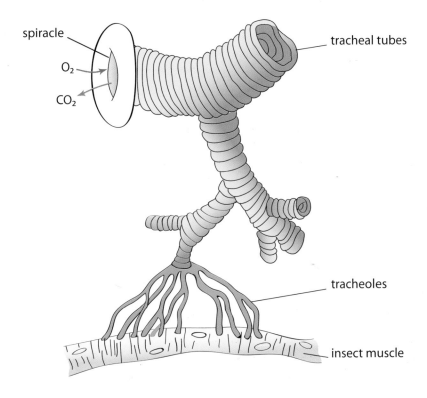

spiracle

O_2

CO_2

tracheal tubes

tracheoles

insect muscle

▲ *Insect branched tracheae*

► *A spiracle from a silkworm*

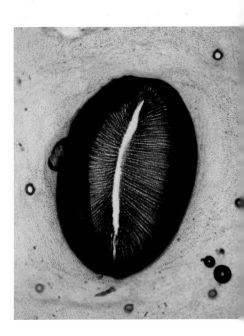

▼ Study point

Most insects possess wings and are extremely efficient in the air. Flight involves a high expenditure of energy and so insects need a good supply of oxygen.

▼ Study point

Although the tracheal system is an efficient method of gas exchange it does have its limitations. To be effective, diffusion requires short pathways. Consequently this limits the size that insects can attain.

YOU SHOULD KNOW ›››

›››the functions of the parts of the respiratory system

›››the essential features of alveoli

›››how gases are exchanged in the alveoli

›››how air is moved into and out of the lungs when breathing in and out

▼ Study point

The diffusion pathway is short as the walls of the alveoli are one cell thick and the blood capillaries have a single layer of endothelial cells.

▼ Study point

The main cause of air being forced out during normal breathing (at rest) is the recoil of the elastic lungs.

22

Knowledge check

Link the appropriate terms 1–5 with the phrases A–E.

1. Bronchi.

2. Intercostals.

3. Alveoli.

4. Trachea.

5. Diaphragm.

A. Flexible airway supported by a ring of cartilage.

B. A sheet of muscle at the base of the thorax.

C. Two branches of the trachea.

D. Air sacs at the end of bronchioles.

E. Muscles located between the ribs.

The human respiratory system

The essential features of exchange surfaces are the same in all organisms and the human is no exception. The lungs supply a large surface area, increased by alveoli, lined with moisture for dissolving gases, thin walls to shorten the diffusion path and an extensive capillary network for rapid diffusion and transport, to maintain diffusion gradients.

The lungs are enclosed within an airtight compartment, the thorax, at the base of which is a dome-shaped sheet of muscle called the diaphragm. The lungs are supported and protected by the rib cage. The ribs can be moved by the intercostal muscles. This enables the lungs to be ventilated so that air is constantly being replenished. Air is drawn into the lungs via flexible airways called trachea. The lungs consist of a branching network of tubes called bronchioles arising from a pair of bronchi.

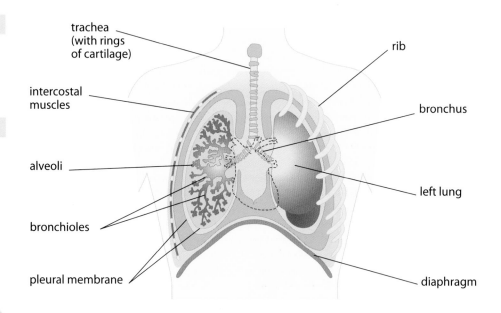

▲ Human respiratory system

Gas exchange in the alveolus

The gas exchange surfaces are the air sacs or alveoli which provide a very large surface area relative to the volume of the body. They are well suited as a gas exchange surface because the walls are thin, providing a short diffusion path. Each alveolus is covered by an extensive capillary network to maintain diffusion gradients, because blood is always taking oxygen away from the alveolus and returning with carbon dioxide.

▶ Alveolus

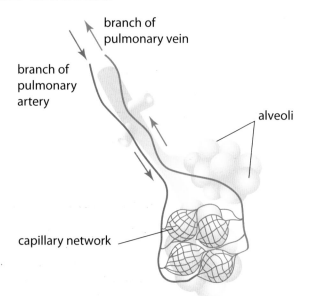

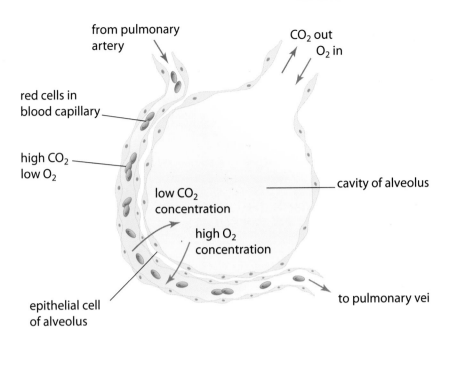

▲ *Gas exchange in alveolus*

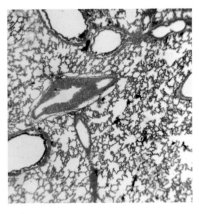

▲ *Lung tissue showing alveoli and blood vessels*

Deoxygenated blood enters the capillaries surrounding the alveolus. Oxygen diffuses out of the alveolus into the blood in the capillary. Carbon dioxide diffuses out of the capillary into the air in the alveolus.

Ventilation of the lungs

Mammals ventilate their lungs by negative pressure breathing, forcing air down into the lungs. That is, if air is to enter the lungs then the pressure inside them must be lower than atmospheric pressure.

Inspiration

Breathing in is an active process since muscle contraction requires energy.

- The external intercostal muscles contract.
- The ribs are pulled upwards and outwards.
- At the same time, the diaphragm muscles contract, causing it to flatten.
- Both actions increase the volume of the thorax.
- This results in a reduction of pressure in the lungs.
- As the atmospheric air pressure is now greater than the pressure in the lungs, air is forced into the lungs.

Expiration

Breathing out is a mainly passive process and is essentially the opposite of inspiration.

Surrounding each lung and lining the thorax are pleural membranes between which is a cavity containing pleural fluid. When breathing, this fluid acts as a lubricant, allowing friction-free movement against the inner wall of the thorax. To prevent the alveoli from collapsing when breathing out, an anti-sticking chemical, called a surfactant, covers their surfaces and reduces the surface tension.

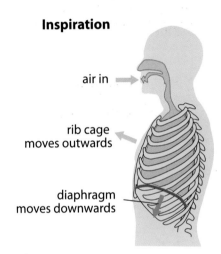

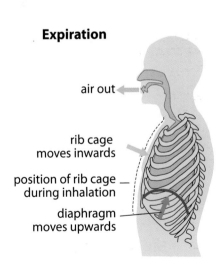

▲ *Movement of ribs and diaphragm during ventilation*

▼ **Study point**

As the rate of photosynthesis is greater than the rate of respiration, during the day the overall gas released is oxygen. At night, only respiration occurs, so the gas released is carbon dioxide.

‹ Link › See micrograph of leaf on page 31.

▼ **Study point**

There is a short diffusion pathway in plants.

Gaseous exchange in plants

In the same way that animals need to respire all the time, so do plants! However, plant cells containing chloroplasts are also capable of carrying out the process of photosynthesis. During the day plants both respire and photosynthesise. Most of the carbon dioxide they need for photosynthesis diffuses into the leaves from the atmosphere. However, some of the carbon dioxide is provided by their respiration. Most of the oxygen produced by photosynthesis diffuses out of leaves. During the night plants respire only and need a supply of oxygen from the atmosphere. Although some oxygen enters the root by diffusion, most gas exchange takes place in the leaves.

The leaf as an organ of gaseous exchange

To enable gaseous exchange to take place efficiently:

- The leaf blade is thin and flat with a large surface area.
- The spongy mesophyll tissue allows for the diffusion of gases.
- The plant tissues are permeated by air spaces.
- The stomatal pores permit gas exchange.

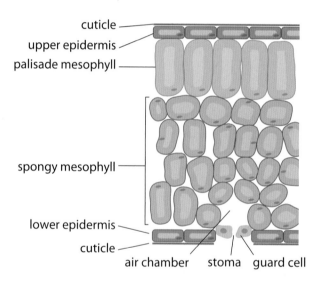

cuticle
upper epidermis
palisade mesophyll
spongy mesophyll
lower epidermis
cuticle
air chamber   stoma   guard cell

▲ *Leaf structure*

Gases diffuse through the stomata along a concentration gradient. Once inside the leaf, the gases in the sub-stomatal air chambers diffuse through the intercellular spaces between the spongy mesophyll cells and into the cells. The direction of diffusion depends on the environmental conditions and the requirements of the plants. It is the net exchange of carbon dioxide and oxygen in relation to respiration and photosynthesis that matters.

Adaptations of the leaf for photosynthesis

To ensure the efficient absorption of light, the leaf shows the following adaptations:

- Leaves have a large surface area to capture as much sunlight as possible.
- Leaves are thin to allow light to penetrate the lower layers of cells.
- The cuticle and epidermis are transparent to allow light to penetrate to the mesophyll.

- Palisade cells are elongated and densely arranged in a layer, or layers.

- The palisade cells are packed with chloroplasts and arranged with their long axes perpendicular to the surface.

- The chloroplasts can rotate and move within the mesophyll cells. This allows them to arrange themselves into the best positions for the efficient absorption of light.

- The intercellular air spaces in the spongy mesophyll allow carbon dioxide to diffuse to the cells, and oxygen can diffuse away.

Stomata

Stomata are small pores found on the lower surface of a leaf. Each pore is bounded by two guard cells. Guard cells are unusual in having chloroplasts and unevenly thickened walls, with the inner wall being thick and the outer wall thin. The stomata control the exchange of gases between the atmosphere and the internal tissues of the leaf.

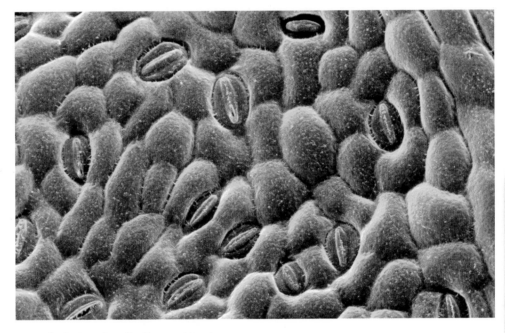

▲ *Surface view of leaf lower epidermis*

Plants also lose water by evaporation though the stomata. This process is called transpiration. Plants wilt if they lose too much water. Sunlight on the upper surface of the leaf would increase evaporation; therefore confining stomata to the lower surface reduces water loss. The presence of a waxy **cuticle** on the upper surface also reduces water loss significantly. In most plants the stomata close at night thus preventing the plant from needlessly losing water when the light intensity is insufficient for photosynthesis to take place.

▼ *Surface view of stomata open and closed*

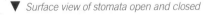

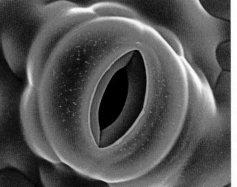
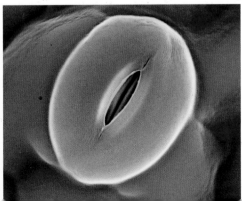

Key Terms

Stoma (plural stomata) = pores located on the lower surface of a leaf, through which gases diffuse.

Cuticle = waxy covering on a leaf which reduces water loss.

▼ Study point

The diffusion gradients in and out of the leaf are maintained by mitochondria carrying out respiration and chloroplasts carrying out photosynthesis.

23

Knowledge check

Link the appropriate terms 1–4 with the phrases A–D.

1. Cuticle.

2. Spongy mesophyll.

3. Palisade mesophyll.

4. Guard cells.

A. Possessing chloroplasts and unevenly thickened walls.

B. Layer of loosely packed cells with air spaces.

C. Layer of cells where photosynthesis occurs.

D. Reduces water loss.

ATP = a compound important in the transfer of energy.

▾ Study point

Plants have to balance the conflicting needs of gas exchange and control of water loss. During periods of excessive water loss stomata may be partly or completely closed.

▾ Study point

The key features of guard cells are that they possess chloroplasts and their cell walls are unevenly thickened.

Examiner tip

The sugar, malate, together with potassium ions, lowers the water potential in guard cells.

The mechanism of opening and closing

It was observed that:

- If water enters the guard cells they swell and the pore opens.

- If water leaves the guard cells they become flaccid and the pore closes.

During the day these changes are thought to be due to the following process:

- The chloroplasts in the guard cells photosynthesise, producing **ATP**.

- This ATP provides energy for an active transport mechanism to take up potassium ions (K^+) from the surrounding epidermal cells into the guard cells.

- Stored starch is converted to malate.

- The water potential in the guard cells is lowered (becomes more negative) and water enters by osmosis.

- The guard cells become turgid and curve apart because their outer walls are thinner than the inner walls, so the pore widens.

The reverse process occurs at night and the pore closes.

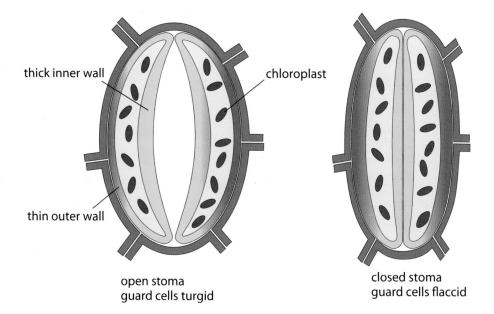

thick inner wall
chloroplast
thin outer wall

open stoma
guard cells turgid

closed stoma
guard cells flaccid

▲ *Stomata open and closed*

▶ *TS stomata*

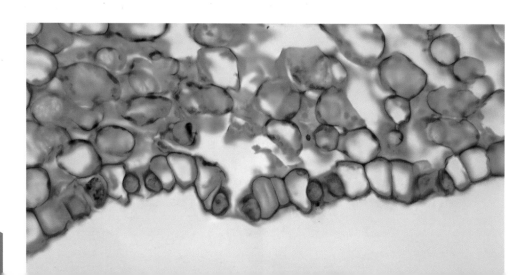

Adaptations for gaseous exchange

1 (a)   Define the term diffusion. (1)

(b)   The drawings illustrate the size and shape of a unicellular organism, *Amoeba*, belonging to the Protoctista, and a multicellular, long, thin, flattened worm, *Planaria*.

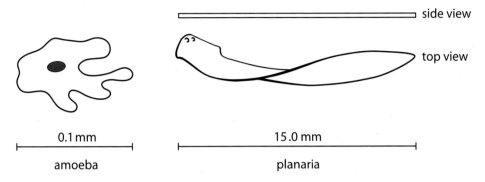

side view

top view

0.1 mm

amoeba

15.0 mm

planaria

For each animal, explain why simple diffusion provides an adequate gaseous exchange between the organism and the environment. (2)

(c)   The table shows various dimensions of cubes of animal tissue:

Length of side (cm)	Volume (cm³)	Ratio of surface area: volume
1	1	6:1
2	8	3:1

(i)   State, in words, the quantitative relationship between length and the surface area/volume ratio. (1)

(ii) Large, multicellular organisms, such as mammals, need a respiratory exchange surface.

I   Name the respiratory exchange surface in a mammal. (1)

II With reference to the table, explain the importance of this exchange surface relating to a mammal. (2)

2 (a)   Multicellular organisms such as fish and mammals have part of their body surface modified to form specialised respiratory surfaces.

(i)   Describe four properties that the respiratory surfaces of fish and mammals have in common. (2)

(ii) Give two advantages to a mammal of having internal lungs. (2)

(b)   Both fish and mammals have ventilation mechanisms.

(i)   Explain the function of ventilation mechanisms. (2)

(ii) Name the muscles which operate the ventilation mechanism in mammals. (2)

3   The diagram represents the mammalian respiratory system.

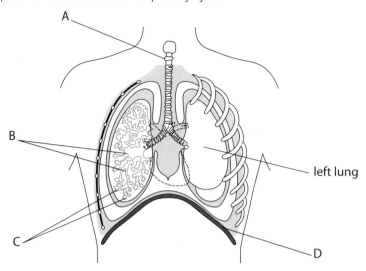

left lung

(a)   Label the structures A–D on the diagram. (4)

(b)   Explain the functions of structures A, C and D. (3)

4 (a)   Insects use a tracheal system for gas exchange.

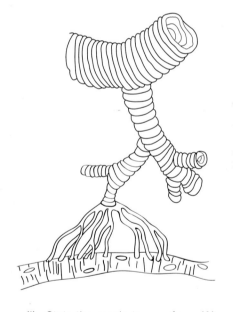

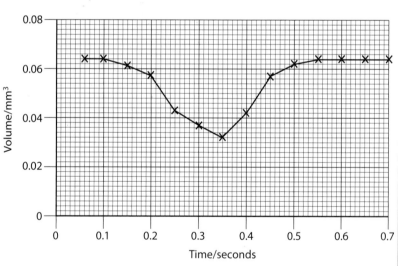

(i)   State the respiratory surface. (1)

(ii)   State two advantages of using the tracheal system for gas exchange. (2)

(iii)   The graph shows the volume change in the main trachea in the anterior thorax and head of a beetle. Calculate the percentage volume change, showing your working. (2)

(b)   Describe and explain the process of inspiration in a mammal. (4)

5 Gas exchange in fish takes place across a special surface, the gill.

(a) State the difficulties aquatic organisms face, compared to terrestrial organisms, in obtaining oxygen from water. (2)

(b) In cartilaginous fish, such as sharks, a parallel flow system operates in the gills; and in bony fish, such as mackerel, a counter-current flow system is found. Explain what is meant by the terms 'parallel flow' and 'counter-current flow' and state why the counter-current system is more efficient. (3)

6 The diagram shows the section of the leaf of a flowering plant. Several features in the diagram indicate how the leaf is adapted to its function. Identify the structures A–D and state the role of each. (8)

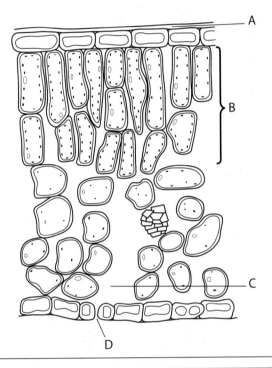

7 The photograph shows the surface view of stomata found on the lower surface of the leaf of *Kalanchoe* sp.

(a) Identify cells A and B. (2)

(b) Give two functions of stomata in leaves. (2)

(c) Explain how the flow of water into cells A leads to the opening of stomatal pores. (4)

(d) When cells A were treated with cyanide the stomatal pores failed to open. Explain why cyanide has this effect on these cells. (2)

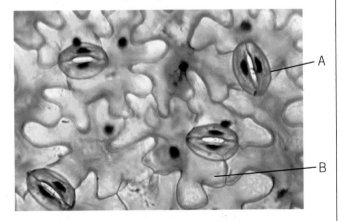

8 Describe the structure of the leaf of a flowering plant, explaining how this structure is adapted to the functions of the leaf. (10)

Transport in animals and plants

Multicellular organisms require a transport system to transfer materials between themselves and the environment. Once taken into the body, materials must be transferred to the cells and once utilised, the waste products returned to the exchange surface for removal. The size and metabolic rate of an organism affects how much material needs to be exchanged.

Both plants and animals need to exchange the gases, carbon dioxide and oxygen. However, as plants make their own food by photosynthesis; their additional requirements are water and mineral salts, which they obtain through the roots. Animals, on the other hand, need to take in nutrients and must remove waste products such as urea.

Topic contents

Transport in animals

By the end of this topic you should be able to:

- Explain why multicellular animals need transport mechanisms.

- Explain the significance and difference between open and closed blood systems and single and double circulations.

- Explain the relationship between the structure and function of arteries, veins and capillaries.

- Describe the cardiac cycle, and interpret graphs showing pressure changes during the cycle.

- Explain the role of the sino-atrial node in initiating heartbeat, and the roles of the atrio-ventricular node and Purkinje tissue in co-ordinating heartbeat.

- Describe the structure of red and white blood cells and the difference between blood, tissue fluid and lymph.

- Describe the role of haemoglobin in the transport of oxygen and carbon dioxide.

- Describe and explain the effects of raised carbon dioxide levels on the haemoglobin dissociation curve.

- Describe the transport of carbon dioxide in terms of the chloride shift.

- Describe the formation of tissue fluid and its importance in exchange of materials.

Features of a transport system

A transport system has the following common features:

- A suitable medium, blood, in which to carry materials.

- A closed system of vessels that contains the blood and forms a branching network to distribute it to all parts of the body.

- A pump, such as the heart, for moving the blood within vessels.

- Valves to maintain the flow in one direction.

- A respiratory pigment (absent in insects) which increases the volume of oxygen that can be transported.

Open systems and closed systems

Insects have an open blood system whereby blood is pumped at relatively low pressure from one main long, dorsal (top) tube-shaped heart running the length of the body. The blood is pumped out of this heart into spaces, collectively called a haemocoel, within the body cavity. The blood bathes the tissues directly, exchange of materials takes place, and there is little control over the direction of circulation. Blood returns slowly to the heart. Here valves and waves of contraction of the muscle wall move the blood forward to the head region where the open circulation is started again. There is no respiratory pigment in the insect as the blood of an insect does not transport oxygen. Oxygen is transported directly to the tissues via the tracheae.

Mammals have a closed circulation system whereby the blood circulates in a continuous system of tubes, the blood vessels. Blood is pumped by a muscular heart at a high pressure resulting in a rapid flow rate. Organs are not in direct contact with the blood but are bathed by tissue fluid seeping out from thin-walled capillaries. The blood contains a blood pigment which carries oxygen.

Even though the earthworm is a relatively simple organism, compared with a mammal it has a closed circulation system. It has dorsal and ventral vessels running the length of the body and these are connected by five 'pseudohearts'. Blood moves through the vessels by the pumping action of the 'pseudohearts'.

Single and double circulations

Closed circulation systems are of two types, depending on whether the blood passes through the heart once or twice in each circulation of the body.

Fish have a single circulation. The heart pumps deoxygenated blood to the gills, oxygenated blood is then carried to the tissues, from there deoxygenated blood returns to the heart. Blood goes once through the heart during each circuit of the body.

▼ *Circulation of fish and mammal*

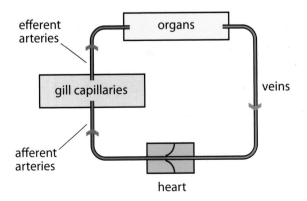

single circulation in fish

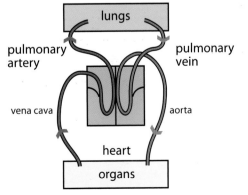

double circulation in mammals

YOU SHOULD KNOW ›››

››› the essential features of a transport system

››› how blood is circulated in mammals

››› the advantages of double circulation

▼ **Study point**

The greater the metabolic rate, the greater the need for rapid transport of glucose and oxygen.

▼ **Study point**

In an open system the blood is pumped into large spaces in the body cavity, whereas in a closed system the blood flows through vessels.

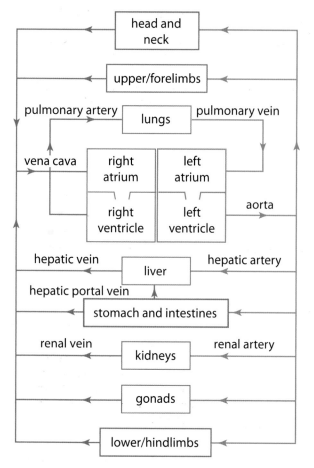

Plan of the mammalian circulatory system

Transport in mammals

Mammals have a double circulatory system. This means that the blood passes twice through the heart for each complete circuit of the body.

When blood is passed to the lungs, its pressure is reduced. If the blood were to pass from the lungs directly to the rest of the body its pressure would make the circulation very slow. Instead the blood is returned to the heart before being pumped to the rest of the body. Materials are then delivered quickly to the body cells to meet metabolic demands.

The double circulatory system may be describes as follows:

- The pulmonary circulation – the right side of the heart pumps deoxygenated blood to the lungs. Oxygenated blood then returns to the left side of the heart.

- Systemic circulation – the left side of the heart pumps the oxygenated blood to the tissues. Deoxygenated blood then returns to the right side of the heart.

- In each circuit the blood passes through the heart twice, once though the right side and once through the left side.

The double circulation of a mammal is more efficient than the single circulation of a fish as oxygenated blood can be pumped around the body at a higher pressure. In fish, pressure is lost in the capillaries of the gills.

◀ *Plan of the mammalian circulatory system*

Structure and function of blood vessels

There are three types of blood vessels: arteries, veins and capillaries.

Arteries and veins have the same basic three-layered structure but the proportions of the different layers vary. In both arteries and veins:

- The innermost layer is the endothelium, which is one cell thick and provides a smooth lining to reduce friction and provide a minimum resistance to the flow of the blood.

- The middle layer is made up of elastic fibres and smooth muscle. This layer is thicker in the arteries than in the veins to accommodate changes in blood flow and pressure as blood is pumped from the heart.

- The outer layer is made up of collagen fibres which are resistant to over-stretching.

▼ *Artery, vein and capillary*

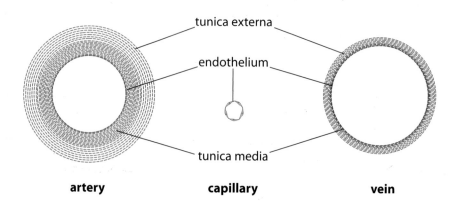

artery   capillary   vein

Examiner tip

You are required to name only the main blood vessels associated with

24

Knowledge check

Match blood vessels 1–5 with descriptions A–E.

1. Pulmonary artery.
2. Aorta.
3. Hepatic portal vein.
4. Vena cava.
5. Pulmonary vein.

A. Carries blood from the stomach to the liver.
B. Joins the right ventricle of the heart to the capillaries of the lungs.
C. Carries oxygenated blood away from the heart to the body.
D. Carries deoxygenated blood from the body to the right atrium of the heart.
E. Carries oxygenated blood from the lungs to the left atrium of the heart.

Arteries carry blood away from the heart. The arteries have thick, muscular walls to withstand the high pressure of blood received from the heart. The contraction of the arterial muscles also helps to maintain pressure as the blood is transported further from the heart.

The arteries branch into smaller vessels called arterioles that further subdivide into thin-walled capillaries. The capillaries form a vast network which penetrates all the tissues and organs of the body. Blood from the capillaries collects into venules, which in turn empty blood into veins, from which it is returned to the heart.

Veins have larger diameters and thinner walls than arteries as the pressure and flow is reduced. Veins have semi-lunar valves along their length to ensure flow in one direction (prevent back flow); these are not present in arteries apart from the aortic valves.

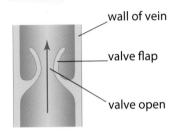

blood flowing towards the heart
passes through the valves

▲ *Vein showing a valve*

The capillaries are thin walled consisting only of a layer of endothelium so their walls are permeable to water and dissolved substances such as glucose. It is at the capillaries that the exchange of materials between the blood and the tissues takes place.

Capillaries have a small diameter and friction with the walls slows the blood flow. Although the diameter is small, there are many capillaries in the capillary bed providing a large total cross-sectional area which further reduces blood flow. This low velocity in very thin-walled vessels enhances their ability to exchange materials with the surrounding tissue fluid.

The heart

LEFT. OXYGENATED
RIGHT. DEOXYGENATED

A pump to circulate blood is an essential feature of a circulatory system. The heart consists of a relatively thin-walled collection chamber, and a thick-walled pumping chamber, which are partitioned into two, allowing the complete separation of oxygenated and deoxygenated blood. The heart is really two separate pumps lying side by side. The pump on the left deals with oxygenated blood and that on the right deals with deoxygenated blood. Each pump has two chambers, the upper atrium and the lower ventricle.

The four-chambered heart consists largely of cardiac muscle, a specialised tissue that is capable of rhythmical contraction and relaxation of its own accord throughout a person's life. The heart muscle is said to be '**myogenic**'.

CARDIAC — muscle
specialised tissue
rhythmical contraction

▶ *Heart*

TRY BEFORE BUY

ATRIUM: ABOVE
VENTRICLES: BELOW

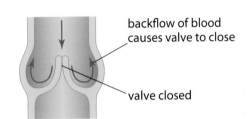

101

Key Terms

Systole = stage in which the heart muscle contracts.

Diastole = stage in which the heart muscle relaxes.

The cardiac cycle

The cardiac cycle describes the sequence of events in one heartbeat. The pumping action of the heart consists of alternating contractions (**systole**) and relaxations (**diastole**). There are three stages to the cardiac cycle.

Atrial systole

The right and left ventricles relax, the tricuspid and bicuspid valves open as the atria contract and blood flows into the ventricles.

Ventricular systole

The atria relax and the right and left ventricles contract together forcing blood out of the heart into the pulmonary artery and the aorta as the semi-lunar valves are opened. The tricuspid and bicuspid valves are closed by the rise in ventricular pressure. The pulmonary artery carries deoxygenated blood to the lungs and the aorta carries oxygenated blood to the various parts of the body.

Diastole

The ventricles relax and the pressure in the ventricles falls. Blood under high pressure in the arteries causes the semi-lunar valves to shut, preventing blood from going back into the ventricles. Blood from the vena cavae and pulmonary veins enters the atria and the cycle starts again.

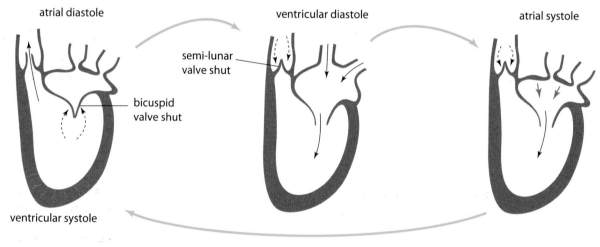

▲ *Cardiac cycle*

The following describes the flow of blood through the left side of the heart.

The left atrium is relaxed and receives oxygenated blood from the pulmonary vein. When full, the pressure forces open the bicuspid valve between the atrium and ventricle. Relaxation of the left ventricle draws blood from the left atrium. The left atrium contracts, pushing the remaining blood into the left ventricle, through the valve. With the left atrium relaxed and with the bicuspid valve closed the left ventricle contracts. The strong muscular walls exert a strong pressure and push blood away from the heart through the semi-lunar valves through the pulmonary arteries and the aorta.

Examiner tip

Don't confuse the cardiac cycle with the control of heartbeat.

- Both sides of the heart work together. Both ventricles contract at the same time, both atria contract together. One complete contraction and relaxation is called a heartbeat.

- After contraction and the compartment has been emptied of blood, it relaxes, to be filled with blood once more.

- The ventricles contain more muscle than the atria and so generate more pressure to force the blood a greater distance.

- The left ventricle has a thicker muscular wall than the right ventricle as it has to pump the blood all round the body whereas the right ventricle has only to pump the blood a shorter distance to the lungs.

Valves

Valves are used to prevent any unwanted backflow of blood. Whether the valves are the atrio-ventricular valves (bicuspid and tricuspid), semi-lunar valves, or the valves in veins, they have the same design and operate in the same way.

Pressure changes in the heart

- The highest pressure occurs in the aorta/arteries that show a rhythmic rise and fall corresponding to ventricular contraction.

- Friction with vessel walls causes a progressive drop in pressure. Arterioles have a large total surface area and a relatively narrow bore causing a substantial reduction from aortic pressure. Their pressure depends on whether they are dilated or contracted.

- The extensive capillary beds have a large cross-sectional area. These beds create an even greater resistance to blood flow.

- There is a relationship between pressure and speed and the pressure drops further due to leakage from capillaries into tissues.

- The return flow to the heart is non-rhythmic and the pressure in the veins is low but can be increased by the massaging effect of muscles.

▼ Changes in pressure

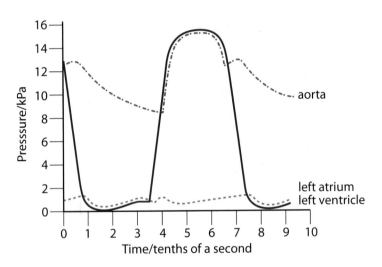

Control of heartbeat

- Cardiac muscle is myogenic.

- Within the wall of the right atrium is a region of specialised cardiac fibres called the sino-atrial node (SAN) that acts as a pacemaker.

- A wave of electrical stimulation arises at this point and then spreads over the two atria causing them to contract more or less at the same time.

- The electrical stimulation is prevented from spreading to the ventricles by a thin layer of connective tissue. This acts as a layer of insulation (it is important that the muscles of the ventricles do not start to contract until the muscles of the atria have finished contracting).

- The stimulation reaches another specialised region of cardiac fibres, the atrio-ventricular node (AVN), which lies between the two atria and which passes on the excitation to specialised tissues in the ventricles.

Examiner tip
The graphical analysis of pressure changes in the heart is a favourite exam question. Be prepared to describe the pressure changes involved in the flow of blood from one chamber of the heart to another together with the associated opening and closing of the valves.

25

Knowledge check

Identify the missing word or words.

The heartbeat is initiated in an area of the right atrium called the ..... The wave of excitation passes across both atria until it reaches an area of tissue in the septum called the ..... This in turn passes the wave to a group of fibres called the .... which transfers the wave to the apex of the ventricles. This causes the ventricles to .... from the base upwards and forces blood to flow out of the heart through the aorta and ....

Examiner tip
The slight delay of the wave of electrical activity at the AVN ensures that the atria are emptied before the ventricles contract.

▼ Control of heartbeat

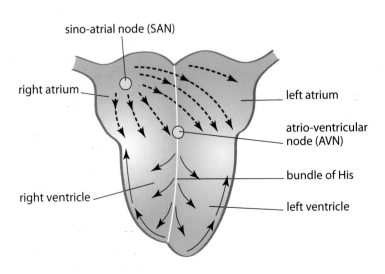

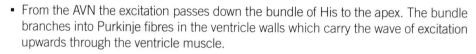

Link Haemoglobin with the quaternary structure of proteins on page 18.

Examiner tip

Relate the structure of red cells to their function of the carriage of oxygen.

26

Knowledge check

Identify the missing word or words.

The blood consists of a pale yellow fluid called •••• which contains red and white blood cells. The red cells or •••• transport •••• combined with haemoglobin as •••• . White blood cells or •••• are of two main types ••••, which engulf bacteria, and •••• which produce antibodies.

- From the AVN the excitation passes down the bundle of His to the apex. The bundle branches into Purkinje fibres in the ventricle walls which carry the wave of excitation upwards through the ventricle muscle.

- The impulses cause the cardiac muscle in each ventricle to contract simultaneously from the apex upwards.

- This ensures that the ventricles are emptied completely.

Blood

Blood is a tissue made up of cells (45%) in fluid plasma (55%).

Red blood cells

Red blood cells (or erythrocytes) contain the pigment haemoglobin, the main function of which is to transport oxygen from the lungs to the respiring tissue. Red blood cells are unusual in two main respects:

- They are biconcave in shape. This increases the surface area of the cell, enabling oxygen to diffuse quickly into or out of the cell.

- They have no nucleus. This means there is more room for haemoglobin, maximising the oxygen that can be carried by each cell.

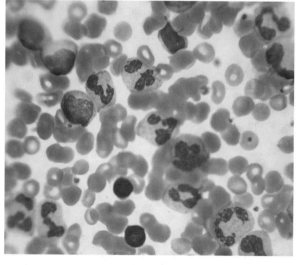

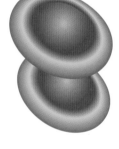

▲ Red and white blood cells under microscope

▲ Two views of red blood cells

White blood cells

White blood cells (or leucocytes) differ from red blood cells in being larger, possessing a nucleus and being either spherical or irregular in shape. There are two groups of white cells:

- Granulocytes, which are phagocytic, have granular cytoplasm, lobed nuclei and engulf bacteria.

- Agranulocytes, which produce antibodies and antitoxins, have clear cytoplasm and spherical nuclei.

Plasma

Plasma is made up largely of 90% water, with soluble food molecules, waste products, hormones, plasma proteins, mineral ions and vitamins dissolved in it. Plasma transports carbon dioxide, digested food products, hormones, plasma proteins, fibrinogen, antibodies, etc., and also distributes heat.

Transport of oxygen

To be efficient at transporting oxygen haemoglobin needs to readily associate with oxygen at the surface where gas exchange is taking place, the lungs, and readily dissociate from oxygen at those tissues, such as muscle, that require it. Haemoglobin is a remarkable molecule that is able to carry out these seemingly contradictory requirements. It is able to change its **affinity** for oxygen in the presence of carbon dioxide by changing its shape. The altered shape binds more loosely with oxygen and releases it.

When a pigment is exposed to increasing **partial pressures of oxygen** it would be expected that it would absorb oxygen evenly and the graph plotted would be a straight line bisecting the two axes. However, samples of haemoglobin exposed to increasing partial pressures of oxygen show an oxygen dissociation curve.

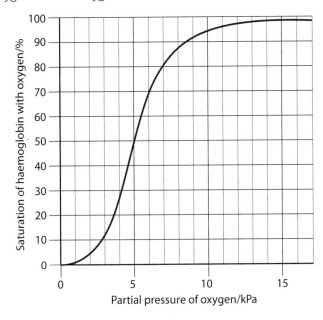

▲ *Graph of oxygen dissociation curve for adult human haemoglobin*

At very low concentrations it is difficult for haemoglobin to absorb oxygen but once loaded it associates readily with oxygen. At high partial pressures of oxygen, the percentage saturation of oxygen is very high.

Red blood cells load oxygen in the lungs where the partial pressure is high and the haemoglobin becomes saturated with oxygen. The cells carry the oxygen as oxyhaemoglobin to the respiring tissues, e.g. muscle, where the partial pressure is low (as oxygen is being used up in respiration to create energy). Oxyhaemoglobin then unloads its oxygen, that is, it dissociates.

The graph also shows that a very small decrease in the partial pressure of oxygen leads to a lot of oxygen becoming dissociated from haemoglobin.

Two facts are important to bear in mind:

- The more the dissociation curve of haemoglobin is displaced to the left, the more readily it picks up oxygen, but the less readily it releases it.

- The more the dissociation curve of haemoglobin is displaced to the right, the less readily it picks up oxygen, but the more easily it releases it.

The effects of carbon dioxide concentration

At higher partial pressure of carbon dioxide the oxygen dissociation curve shifts to the right. This phenomenon is known as the **Bohr effect**. When oxygen reaches respiring tissues, such as muscle, the high partial pressure of carbon dioxide there, enables haemoglobin to unload its oxygen even more readily.

Key Terms

Affinity = one molecule having a chemical attraction for another.

Partial pressure (of oxygen (pO$_2$)) = normal atmospheric pressure is 100kPa. As oxygen makes up 21% of the atmosphere its maximum partial pressure is 21kPa.

Bohr effect = at higher partial pressures of carbon dioxide the more the curve shifts to the right.

▼ Study point

When referring to the combination of oxygen with haemoglobin, use the terms loading or associating. When referring to haemoglobin releasing its oxygen use the terms unloading or dissociating.

▼ Study point

Haemoglobin has a reduced affinity for oxygen in the presence of carbon dioxide.

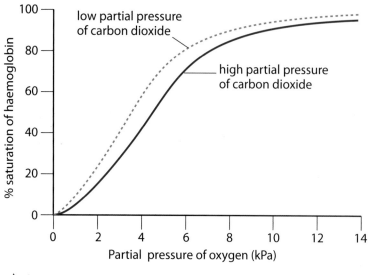

Graph showing Bohr effect

In summary:

- When the respiratory pigment haemoglobin is exposed to a gradual increase in oxygen tension it absorbs oxygen rapidly at first but more slowly as the tension continues to rise. This relationship is known as the oxygen dissociation curve.

- The release of oxygen from haemoglobin is facilitated by the presence of carbon dioxide, when the partial pressure of oxygen is high, as in the lung capillaries, oxygen combines with the haemoglobin to form oxyhaemoglobin.

- When the partial pressure of oxygen is low, as found in the respiring tissues, then the oxygen dissociates from the haemoglobin.

- When the partial pressure of carbon dioxide is high, haemoglobin is less efficient at associating with oxygen and more efficient at releasing it.

The dissociation curve of foetal haemoglobin

The blood of the foetus and the mother flow closely together in the placenta but rarely mix. To enable the foetal haemoglobin to absorb oxygen from the maternal haemoglobin in the placenta the foetus has a haemoglobin that differs (in two of the four polypeptide chains) from the haemoglobin of the adult. This structural difference makes the foetal haemoglobin dissociation curve shift to the left of that of the adult. The foetal haemoglobin combines with oxygen more readily than does the mother's haemoglobin. That is, the foetal haemoglobin has a greater affinity for oxygen.

Transport of oxygen in other animals

Many organisms possess haemoglobin and often have different forms of haemoglobin. This has been found to be related to the habitat in which they live. Some animals have become adapted to living in habitats where there are low levels of oxygen.

▼ *Comparison of lugworm and human dissociation curves*

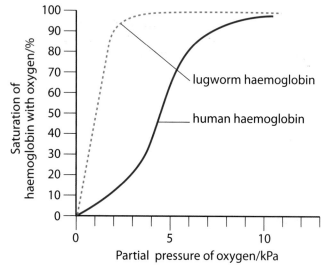

The lugworm has a low metabolic rate and lives in the sand on the seashore (worm casts can be seen at low tide). The lugworm pumps seawater through its burrow, giving access to the limited amount of dissolved oxygen present. To enable it to load the oxygen more readily it has haemoglobin with a dissociation curve very much to the left compared with a human haemoglobin dissociation curve.

With increase in altitude there is a drop in atmospheric pressure. This is significant for animals, such as the llama, because the partial pressure of oxygen in the atmosphere is less at high altitude. To compensate for this the llama possesses haemoglobin which loads more readily with oxygen in the lungs. Haemoglobin of this sort has a dissociation curve to the left of normal haemoglobin.

Myoglobin

Myoglobin is far more stable than haemoglobin and will not release its oxygen unless the partial pressure of oxygen is extremely low. The dissociation curve of myoglobin is far to the left of that of haemoglobin. At each partial pressure of oxygen, myoglobin has a higher percentage oxygen saturation than haemoglobin. Normally, the respiring muscle obtains its oxygen from haemoglobin. However, if the oxygen partial pressure becomes very low, as when exercising, the oxymyoglobin unloads its oxygen. The oxygen held by the myoglobin acts as a reserve, to be used only in conditions of particular oxygen demand, such as sustained activity.

▼ Study point

At high altitude the number of red cells in the blood of mammals increases.

Transport of carbon dioxide

Carbon dioxide is transported in blood cells and plasma in three ways:

- In solution in the plasma (5%).

- As hydrogen carbonate (85%).

- In combination with haemoglobin to form carbamino-haemoglobin (10%).

Some carbon dioxide is transported in the red blood cells but most is converted in the red blood cells to hydrogen carbonate, which is then dissolved in the plasma.

The following describes a series of reactions known as the chloride shift:

- Carbon dioxide diffuses into the red blood cell (RBC) and combines with water to form carbonic acid. The reaction is catalysed by carbonic anhydrase.

- Carbonic acid dissociates into H^+ and HCO_3^- ions. HCO_3^- ions diffuse out of the RBC into the plasma where they combine with Na^+ ions from the dissociation of sodium chloride to form sodium hydrogen carbonate.

- H^+ ions provide the conditions for the oxyhaemoglobin to dissociate into oxygen and haemoglobin.

- H^+ ions are buffered by their combination with haemoglobin and the formation of haemoglobinic acid (HHb).

- The oxygen diffuses out of the RBC into the tissues.

- To balance the outward movement of negatively charged ions, chloride ions diffuse in.

- It is by this means that the electrochemical neutrality of the RBC is maintained.

▼ *Summary of chloride shift*

▼ **Study point**

The chloride shift refers to the influx of chloride ions into the red blood cells to preserve electrical neutrality.

Examiner tip
Only use abbreviations such as RBC once you have used the term in full.

▼ **Study point**

Haemoglobin acts as a buffer helping to maintain the blood pH by removing hydrogen ions from solution.

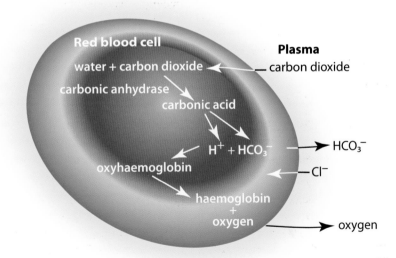

Intercellular fluid

The capillaries are the site of exchange between the blood and the cells of the body. They are well adapted to allow the exchange of materials between the blood and the cells:

- They have thin, permeable walls.

- They provide a large surface area for exchange of materials.

- Blood flows very slowly through the capillaries allowing time for exchange of materials.

Key Term

Tissue fluid = plasma minus plasma proteins.

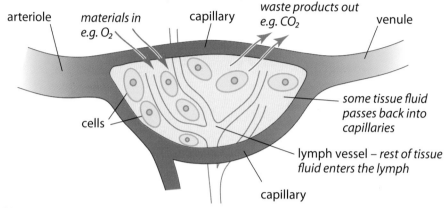

► *Capillary network*

▼ **Study point**

The two opposing forces involved in the formation of tissue fluid are hydrostatic pressure and water potential.

Blood consists of the fluid plasma that carries the blood cells, dissolved materials and large molecules, called plasma proteins. The blood is contained in a closed system but fluid from the plasma escapes through the walls of the capillaries. This fluid is called **tissue fluid** and bathes the cells, supplying them with glucose, amino acids, fatty acids, salts and oxygen. The tissue fluid also removes waste materials from the cells.

- The factors responsible for the movements of solutes and water into and out of the capillaries are blood pressure and diffusion.

- When blood reaches the arterial end of a capillary it is under pressure because of the pumping action of the heart and the resistance to blood flow of the capillaries. This hydrostatic pressure forces the fluid part of the blood through the capillary walls into the spaces between the cells.

- This outward flow is opposed by the reduced water potential of the blood, created by the presence of the plasma proteins.

- The hydrostatic pressure of the blood is greater than the osmotic forces so there is a net flow of water and solutes out of the blood.

- At the arterial end of the capillary bed the diffusion gradient for solutes such as glucose, oxygen and ions favours movement from the capillaries to the tissue fluid. This is because these substances are being used during cell metabolism.

- At the venous end of the capillary bed the blood pressure is lower and water passes into the capillaries by osmosis. The reduced water potential of the blood created by the presence of the plasma proteins causes a net inflow of water.

- At the venous end tissue fluid picks up CO_2 and other excretory substances. Some of this fluid passes back into the capillaries, but some drains into the lymphatic system and is returned eventually to the venous system via the thoracic duct, which empties into a vein near the heart.

27

Knowledge check

Match the terms 1–4 with descriptions A–D.

1. Bohr effect.

2. Tissue.

3. Chloride shift.

4. Haemoglobin.

A. The means by which the electrochemical neutrality of the red blood cell is maintained.

B. The fluid involved in the exchange of materials, between blood and body cells.

C. The blood pigment that carries oxygen in mammals.

D. At higher partial pressures of carbon dioxide the oxygen dissociation curve shifts to the right.

▼ *Hydrostatic and opposing osmotic force*

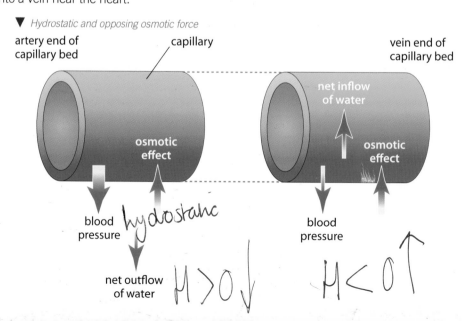

BY2 Transport in animals and plants

Roots absorb water from the soil and this water needs to be transported some distance to the leaves, where it is used in the process of photosynthesis. In turn, the sugar produced must be transported to where it is needed. Plants have evolved two distinct systems of tubes: the xylem to transport water and phloem to transport sugars.

Transport in plants

By the end of this topic you should be able to:

- Explain why plants need a transport system.

- Describe the distribution of xylem and phloem in roots and stems.

- Describe the structure of xylem vessels and phloem sieve tubes and relate these cells to their functions.

- Describe the uptake of water by the root.

- Describe the pathway and mechanisms involved in the movement of water from root to leaf.

- Describe the structure and role of the endodermis.

- Describe transpiration and explain how environmental factors affect its rate.

- Explain the adaptations of hydrophytes and xerophytes in relation to prevailing water supply.

- Explain how translocation of organic solutes occurs in plants.

Structure and distribution of vascular tissue

A vascular bundle is made up of two main tissues: xylem and phloem. They are distributed differently in roots, stems and leaves.

- In roots the xylem is arranged centrally. This arrangement is ideal for resistance to vertical stresses (pull) and so helps the anchorage of the plant.

- In stems xylem is arranged in vascular bundles that are placed in a ring at the periphery. This organisation gives flexible support but also resistance to bending strain.

- In leaves the arrangement of vascular tissues in the midrib and network of veins also gives flexible strength and resistance to tearing strains.

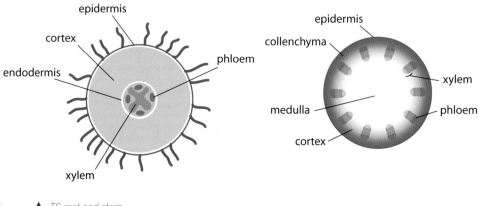

▲ TS root and stem

The structure of xylem

The main cell types in xylem are vessels and tracheids.

Vessels and tracheids form a system of tubes through which water can travel. As they mature and differentiate, their cellulose cell walls incorporate lignin, which is a very hard, strong substance. As it builds up around the cell the contents die, leaving an empty space inside. The end walls break down so that the cells form a continuous tube. The deposition of lignin strengthens the wall and also makes the walls impermeable to water and solutes. Xylem vessels therefore have two functions, transport and providing mechanical strength and support to the plant.

▶ **Study point**

As diffusion would be too slow to supply the needs of multicellular plants, a mass flow system is required. Plants have evolved two distinct systems of tubes: xylem to transport water and mineral salts, and phloem to transport sucrose and amino acids.

Examiner tip
Be prepared to identify cell types in an examination.

Link The structure of phloem is discussed under the topic of translocation on page 117.

Link Transpiration is studied in detail on page 113.

 ▼ LS xylem

 ▼ TS xylem

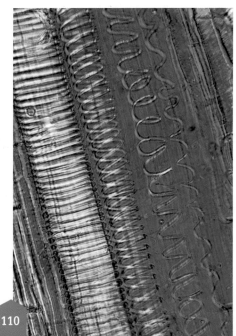

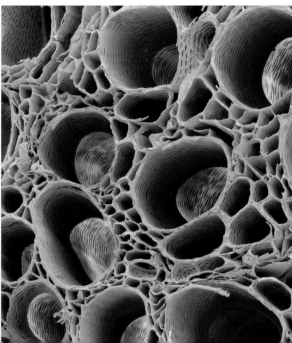

Transport in the xylem (dead cells)

Water uptake by the roots

Terrestrial plants have the same problem as terrestrial animals. They need to conserve water but water is needed to carry out the process of photosynthesis that takes place in the leaves. Water has to be drawn up from the soil through the roots and transported to the leaves, where some of the water is used in photosynthesis and the rest is lost through the stomata. The large loss of water through the stomata of the leaves by the process of **transpiration** must constantly be replaced with water from the soil. The region of greatest uptake is the root hair zone where the surface area of the root is enormously increased by the presence of root hairs.

Key Term

Transpiration = The evaporation of water from inside the leaves, through the stomata to the atmosphere.

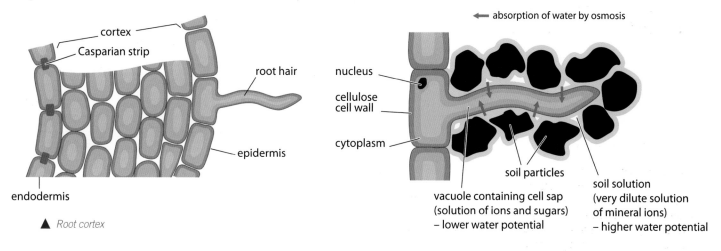

◀ *Root cortex*

◀ *Absorption of water by root hair cell*

The soil water contains a very weak solution of mineral salts and so has a high water potential. The vacuole of the root hair cell contains a strong solution of dissolved substances and has a low water potential. Water passes into the root hair cell down a water potential (WP) gradient from a high WP to a low WP by osmosis. Water can travel across the cells of the cortex of the root along three pathways:

- The apoplast – through the cell wall.

- The symplast – through the cytoplasm and plasmodesmata.

- The vacuolar pathway – from vacuole to vacuole.

However, it is considered that the two main pathways are the symplast and apoplast pathways. Most of the water probably follows the latter pathway as this is the faster of the two.

▼ *Pathways of water transport across cortex*

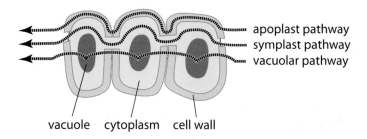

apoplast pathway
symplast pathway
vacuolar pathway

vacuole   cytoplasm   cell wall

▼ Study point

A water potential gradient exists across the cortex. The WP is high in the root hair cell and lower in the adjacent cells.

Key Terms

Endodermis = a ring of cells surrounding the xylem tissue having an impermeable waterproof barrier through their cell walls.

Root pressure = a force created at the base of the xylem vessel by the influx of water along a water potential gradient.

Cohesion = water molecules tend to stick together.

Adhesion = the water molecules stick to the walls of the xylem.

Capillarity = the tendency for water to rise in narrow tubes.

28

Knowledge check

Identify the missing word or words.

Water is taken up from the soil mainly through specialised cells called •••• •••• cells. Water passes across the root cortex down a •••• •••• gradient. The water passes mainly along two pathways, the •••• and apoplast pathways. On reaching the endodermis a band of suberin called the •••• •••• prevents the use of the apoplast pathway.

Tension is highest during day because of more movement of water, increasing pressure which high tension.

The xylem tissue is found in the centre of the root and is surrounded by a single layer of cells called the **endodermis**. The cell walls of the endodermis are impregnated with a waxy material called suberin. This forms a distinctive band known as the Casparian strip. The suberin is waterproof and the Casparian strip prevents the use of the apoplast pathway. The only way that water can pass across the endodermis to the xylem is along the symplast pathway. Active transport of salts is the most likely mechanism by which water enters the xylem from the endodermal cells. This explains why the water must first enter the cytoplasm of the endodermal cells. The active transport of mineral ions into the xylem by the endodermal cells lowers the water potential in the xylem. Water now moves into the xylem, by osmosis, along a water potential gradient. The water potential gradient produced creates a force known as the **root pressure**.

Casparian strip

direction in which water passes through endodermal cell

▲ *Endodermal cell showing the Casparian strip*

Uptake of minerals

Generally, minerals are taken up by the root hairs by active transport from the soil solution. Once absorbed, the mineral ions may move along the apoplast pathway carried in solution by the water being pulled up the plant in the transpiration stream. When minerals reach the endodermis the Casparian strip prevents further movement along the cell walls. The ions enter the cytoplasm of the cell from where they diffuse or are actively transported into the xylem. For example, nitrogen usually enters the plant as nitrate ions/ammonium ions which diffuse along the concentration gradient into the apoplast stream but enter the symplast by active transport against the concentration gradient and then flow via plasmodesmata in the cytoplasmic stream.

At the endodermis, ions must be actively taken up to by-pass the Casparian band which allows the plant to selectively take up the ions at this point.

The movement of water from roots to the leaves

The main force that pulls water up the stem is transpiration. This is a passive process and does not require energy to take place.

- Water travels in the xylem up through the stem to the leaves, where most of it evaporates from the internal leaf surface and passes out, as water vapour, into the atmosphere.

- The transpiration of water from the leaves draws water across the leaf from the xylem tissue along the same three pathways as in the root.

- As water molecules leave xylem cells in the leaf, they pull up other water molecules. This pulling effect is known as the transpiration pull and is possible because of the large **cohesive** forces between water molecules and the **adhesive** forces which exist between the water molecules and the hydrophilic lining of the vessels. These two forces combine to maintain the column of water in the xylem.

NEGATIVE PRESSURE

- The theory of the mechanism by which water moves up the xylem is known as the Cohesion-Tension theory.

- **Capillarity** is another force that may contribute to the rise of water in the xylem. Water rises up narrow tubes by capillary action but this force is probably of more relevance in small plants than large trees.

THERE IS NO DIFFERENCE OF WP IN XYLEM

low pressure because water is leaving

pressure change due to water moving out of leaf.

water is drawn up the transpiration stream as a result of the cohesive forces between water molecules

high pressure but pressure forcing water over.

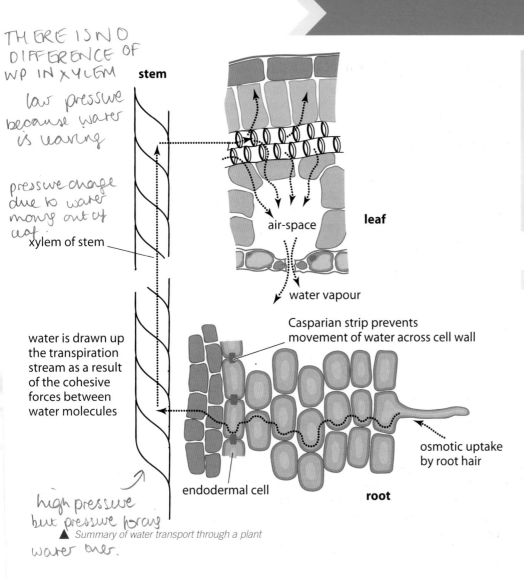
▲ Summary of water transport through a plant

stem

leaf

air-space

water vapour

Casparian strip prevents movement of water across cell wall

xylem of stem

osmotic uptake by root hair

endodermal cell

root

▼ Study point

There are three main forces involved in water transport from root to leaf: root pressure, which is a 'push'; transpiration 'pull'; and capillarity.

Examiner tip

The transport of water is an extensive topic. In an exam it often appears as an essay question. Read the question carefully to make sure you provide only the relevant material.

Transpiration

Land plants continually lose water vapour to the atmosphere. In fact, about 99% of the water absorbed by the plant can be lost by evaporation through the leaves. This evaporation of water from inside the leaves through the stomata to the atmosphere is known as transpiration and gives rise to the transpiration stream. All plants have to balance water uptake with water loss. If a plant loses more water than it absorbs, it wilts. If a plant loses an excessive quantity of water, it reaches a point where it cannot regain its turgor and it dies.

Plants face a dilemma. The stomata need to be open during the day to allow the exchange of gases between the tissues of the leaf and the atmosphere. However, the presence of pores in the leaves means that valuable water is lost from the plant. Most of the water is lost through the stomata, although around 5% of the total water vapour loss can occur through the leaf epidermis. This loss is normally reduced due to the presence of the waxy cuticle on the surface of the leaves.

▶ Movement of water out of leaf

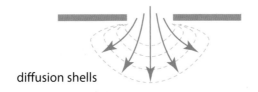

diffusion shells

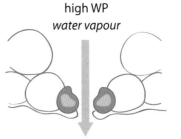
high WP
water vapour

low WP in atmospheric air

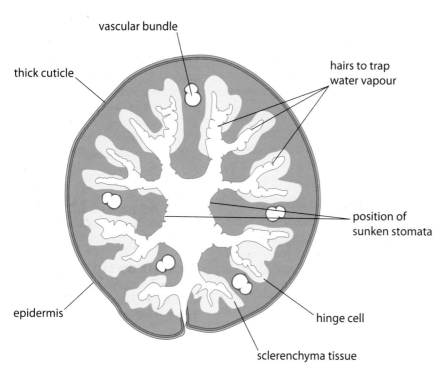

vascular bundle

thick cuticle

hairs to trap
water vapour

position of
sunken stomata

epidermis

hinge cell

sclerenchyma tissue

▲ *Marram grass*

Marram grass shows the following modifications:

- Rolled leaves – large thin-walled epidermal cells at the bases of the grooves shrink when they lose water from excessive transpiration, causing the leaf to roll onto itself. This has the effect of reducing the leaf area from which transpiration can occur.

- Sunken stomata – stomata are found in grooves on the inner side of the leaf. They are located in pits or depressions so that humid air is trapped outside the stomata. This reduces the water potential gradient between the leaf and the atmosphere and so reduces the rate of diffusion of water.

- Hairs – stiff, interlocking hairs trap water vapour and reduce the water potential gradient.

- Thick cuticle – the cuticle is a waxy covering over the leaf surface which reduces water loss. The thicker this cuticle, the lower the rate of cuticular transpiration.

Hydrophytes

Hydrophytes grow submerged or partially submerged in water. An example is the water lily, which is rooted to the mud at the bottom of a pond and has floating leaves on the surface of the water. Hydrophytes are adapted as follows:

- As water is a supportive medium they have little or no lignified support tissues.

- Surrounded by water there is little need for transport tissue, so xylem is poorly developed.

- Leaves have little or no cuticle.

- Stomata are found on the upper surface of the leaves.

- Stems and leaves have large air spaces, forming a reservoir of oxygen and carbon dioxide. These gases also provide buoyancy to the plant tissues when submerged.

29

Knowledge check

Identify the missing word or words.

Water evaporates from the air spaces of a leaf by a process called ••••, which takes place mainly through pores called •••• located in the lower epidermis. Plants which live in conditions of low water availability are called ••••. Typically they have •••• stomata and a thick waxy •••• which reduces water loss. Plants growing submerged in water are called ••••.

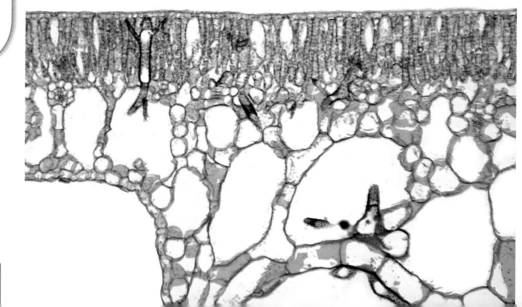

► *Hydrophyte*

Translocation — movement of sugars made in photosynthesis

The products of photosynthesis are transported in the phloem, away from the site of synthesis in the leaves, the 'source', to all the other parts of the plant where they are used for growth or storage, the 'sinks'. In plants the transport of the soluble organic materials, sucrose and amino acids, is known as translocation.

Structure of phloem

Phloem is a living tissue and consists of several types of cells, the main ones being sieve tubes and companion cells.

The sieve tubes are the only components of phloem obviously adapted for the longitudinal flow of material. They are formed from cells called sieve elements placed end to end. The end walls do not break down but are perforated by pores. These areas are known as sieve plates. Cytoplasmic filaments containing phloem protein extend from one sieve cell to the next through the pores in the sieve plate. The sieve tubes do not possess a nucleus and during their development most of the other cell organelles disintegrate. Each sieve tube element is closely associated with at least one companion cell, which has dense cytoplasm, large centrally placed nuclei, many mitochondria, and they are connected to the sieve tube element by plasmodesmata.

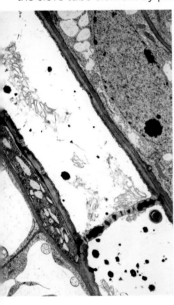
▲ *LS phloem*

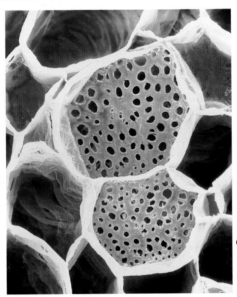
▲ *Sieve plate*

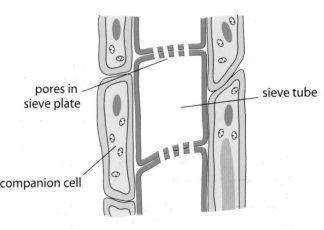

pores in sieve plate

sieve tube

companion cell

▲ *Phloem tissue*

Transport in the phloem (living cells) → travels all over plant

Experimental evidence suggests that the phloem is the tissue concerned with the translocation of organic substances. Several different techniques have been used:

- Early evidence was obtained from ringing experiments where cylinders of outer bark tissue (removing the phloem) were removed from woody stems and the contents of the phloem above and below the cylinder were later analysed.

- More recently, the technique of radioactive tracing with labelled metabolites using aphids, has been used. An aphid has needle-like mouthparts forming a hollow tube-like stylet. This is inserted into sieve tubes to feed on the sap. To sample the phloem sap the aphid is anaesthetised and the stylet is cut off, leaving it attached to the plant. As the sap is under pressure it exudes from the very fine tube and can be collected and analysed. These experiments have enabled scientists to demonstrate that translocation is a rapid process, much too rapid to be explained by diffusion.

▼ **Study point**

Draw up a table of comparison between xylem vessels and sieve tubes.

Examiner tip

Sucrose and amino acids are transported in the phloem. It is incorrect to state that it is sugar that is transported.

How Science Works

The mechanism of translocation in a plant has not been satisfactorily explained. The mass flow theory suggests a passive process is involved but more recent work suggests an active process is involved.

- Radioisotope labelling is a technique where carbon dioxide labelled with radioactive carbon is supplied to an illuminated plant leaf. The radioactive carbon is fixed in the sugar produced in photosynthesis and its translocation to other parts of the plant can be traced using autoradiography. The 'source' leaf and 'sink' tissues are placed firmly on photographic film in the dark for 24 hours. When the film is developed, the presence of radioactivity in parts of the tissue shows up as 'fogging' of the negatives. The technique shows that the sugar is transported in both an upward and downward direction, since the radioactivity is shown in the aerial parts of the plant as well as the roots. An autoradiograph of a transverse section of a stem of a treated plant shows fogging only where phloem was in contact with the film.

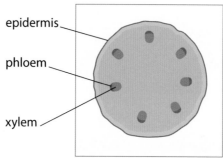
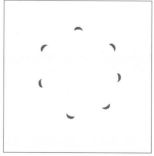

section of stem placed against photographic film in the dark

developed film emulsion is fogged by the presence of radioactivity in the phloem

▲ *Autoradiograph*

Theories of translocation

The main theory put forward to explain the transport of organic solutes is known as the mass flow hypothesis (1937). This theory suggests that there is a passive mass flow of sugars from the phloem of the leaf, where there is the highest concentration (the source), to other areas, such as growing tissues, where there is a lower concentration (the sink).

The diagram shows a mass flow model:

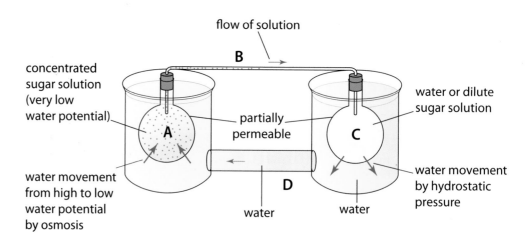

▲ *Mass flow*

Region A represents leaf cells, a source of sugar made in photosynthesis.

C represents a sink where sugar is removed.

B represents the phloem which joins the source to the sink.

D represents the xylem bringing water back to the source.

When sugar is made at A the water potential becomes more negative and water passes in by osmosis. Water also passes into C but to a lesser extent than into A, since it has a much higher water potential. As water enters A, hydrostatic pressure builds up forcing the sugar in solution into B. Mass flow of the solution takes place along B into C. This forces water out of C into D.

There are a number of arguments against the mass flow theory. These include:

- The rate of transport in phloem is about 10,000 times faster than it would be if substances were moving by diffusion.

- It does not explain the existence of the sieve plates which seemingly act as a series of barriers impeding flow.

- Sucrose and amino acids have been observed to move at different rates and in different directions in the same tissue.

- Phloem tissue has a relatively high rate of oxygen consumption, and translocation is slowed down or stopped altogether if respiratory poisons such as potassium cyanide enter the phloem.

- The companion cells contain numerous mitochondria and produce energy but the mass flow hypothesis fails to suggest a role for the companion cells.

Recent theories have been put forward suggesting:

- An active process may be involved.

- The observation of streaming in the cytoplasm of individual sieve tubes could be responsible for bi-directional movements along individual sieve tubes, providing there was some mechanism to transport solutes across the sieve plates.

- Different solutes are transported along different routes, since it has been observed that protein filaments pass through the sieve pores.

30

Knowledge check

Identify the missing word or words.

Translocation is the transport of organic solutes such as •••• and amino acids away from the site of synthesis in the leaf, which is called the '••••', to all the other parts of the plant where they are used for growth or storage, the '••••'. The products of photosynthesis are transported in the phloem cells known as •••• •••• .

▼ Study point

You are not required to give details of any of these theories.

▶ *Sources and sinks in mass flow*

source cell, e.g. mesophyll cell of leaf where sugar is formed

high hydrostatic pressure here due to dissolved sugar

water loss by evaporation

sugar loaded into sieve tubes

transpiration stream

water flow along sieve elements from high to low hydrostatic pressure zone

xylem

water uptake in root hair

low hydrostatic pressure here because sugar is converted to insoluble starch

sink cell e.g. starch storage cell

BY2

Reproductive strategies

The life cycle of an organism may be defined as the sequence of changes through which it passes during its life, from its origin in reproduction until its death. For a species to survive it must produce new individuals.

Reproduction is the ability to produce other individuals of the same species and is a fundamental characteristic of living things. New individuals may be produced by either asexual or sexual reproduction, or in some species by both methods. In animals, asexual reproduction is far less common than it is in plants, protoctists and prokaryotes.

Topic contents

By the end of this topic you should be able to:

- Describe the principles of asexual and sexual reproduction in plants and animals.
- Describe their relative advantages and disadvantages.
- Describe the adaptations of different vertebrate groups to life on land.
- Describe the importance of internal fertilisation and development to terrestrial organisms.
- Describe insects as a successful land-colonising group.
- Describe incomplete and complete metamorphosis in insects.
- Compare the reproductive strategies of plants and animals.
- Give reasons for the success of flowering plants.

Asexual and sexual reproduction

In plants and animals reproduction is achieved in two ways. Some organisms, such as bacteria and yeast, reproduce asexually; more advanced animals reproduce only sexually; flowering plants can reproduce both asexually and sexually.

Asexual reproduction

Asexual reproduction results in the rapid production of large numbers of individuals having an identical genetic composition. A group of genetically identical offspring produced by this method is called a **clone**. Examples of asexual methods in animals include binary fission and budding. Plant examples are bulbs, e.g. daffodil; runners, e.g. strawberry; tubers, e.g. potato.

Sexual reproduction

Sexual reproduction usually involves two parents, is less rapid than asexual and produces offspring that are genetically different. Diploid body cells produce haploid sex cells or gametes. The fusion of haploid gametes is always involved.

The advantages and disadvantages of asexual and sexual reproduction

In asexual reproduction lack of variety is a disadvantage in adapting to environmental change but its main advantage is that if an individual has a genetic makeup suited to a particular set of conditions, large numbers of this successful type may be built up.

Although sexual reproduction is a slower process, there are a number of advantages:

- There is an increase in genetic variety so enabling a species to adapt to environmental change.

- It allows the development of a resistant stage in the life cycle, which enables the species to withstand adverse conditions.

- The formation of spores, seeds, and larvae enables the dispersal of offspring. This reduces intra-specific competition and so enables genetic variety to develop as required.

▶ *Life cycle of the frog*

Key Term

Clone = a group of genetically identical offspring produced by asexual means.

 Link Cell division on page 60.

▼ **Study point**

Mutations, although rare, help to create a little variety in asexual reproduction. Mutations arise more frequently (but still rarely) during sexual reproduction because of the greater complexity of the process.

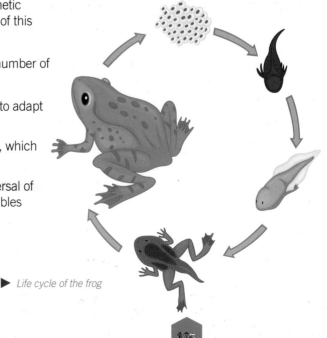

Gamete production and fertilisation

Gamete production

- Sexually reproducing organisms have **diploid** body cells and **haploid** sex cells or gametes.

- Body cells with the full chromosome number are produced by mitosis.

- Haploid cells with half the chromosome number are produced by meiosis.

- At **fertilisation** the haploid sperm fuses with a haploid egg to produce a diploid fertilised egg. The **zygote** formed then divides many times by mitosis to grow into a new individual.

Males and females usually produce different-sized gametes. The male gamete is small and extremely motile and the female gamete is large and sedentary, normally due to the presence of stored food.

Mammalian eggs differ in that they contain very little stored food, and instead the materials for development are obtained from the maternal blood supply through the placenta.

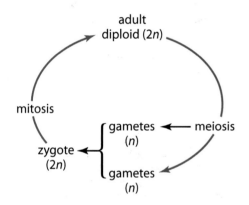

◀ *Diploid life cycle*

Fertilisation

Many aquatic organisms discharge their gametes directly into the sea or freshwater. As the gametes are quickly dispersed by the water, there is a strong possibility that many eggs will not encounter sperm. In animals this kind of fertilisation is known as external fertilisation. There is a considerable wastage and so large numbers of gametes of both sexes have to be produced. In the frog, the joining of sperm and egg is facilitated by a sexual coupling. When the eggs are laid by the female, the male immediately releases seminal fluid over them. While amphibians, in general, can move efficiently on land, many must return to water to reproduce and fertilisation is external.

In most terrestrial animals, however, fertilisation occurs inside the body of the female and this is called internal fertilisation. Generally, this requires the use of some kind of intromittent organ to introduce the sperm into the female's body.

Internal fertilisation has several advantages. There is less chance of gametes being wasted. It allows the male gamete to become independent of the need for water for movement. The fertilised egg can be enclosed within a protective covering before it leaves the female's body. This is what happens in animals that lay eggs. Some animals take this idea further and the embryos develop within the female parent and derive nourishment from her. This reaches its greatest development in those mammals that nourish their developing young before birth by means of a placenta.

Adaptations of organisms to life on land

In many animals the fertilised egg or zygote undergoes development outside the body of the parent. The developing offspring are easy prey for predators and provide food for other species. Many eggs are produced to ensure that at least a few survive. In insects, although fertilisation is internal, the fertilised eggs are normally laid on a suitable food source and the embryo develops outside the body. Internal fertilisation ensures that all the sperm are deposited in the female's reproductive tract.

The gradual adaptation to life on land includes the evolution of eggs in reptiles and birds. The egg has a fluid-filled cavity surrounded by a membrane outside which is a protective shell, which encloses the embryo within the yolk sac. Birds incubate eggs and the embryo completes its development outside the mother's body.

In mammals the young are retained for a considerable time in the mother's womb or uterus but there is no shell. The embryo is nourished there from the mother's blood supply via the placenta. The young are born in a relatively advanced state of development.

Parental care

Many animal species reproduce by laying fertilised eggs that are left to develop unattended. There is little or no parental care. Others provide some sort of parental care, e.g. the male stickleback looks after the fertilised eggs in a defended territory and fans them to provide oxygen until they hatch and swim away. Pronounced parental care is typical of most species of birds and mammals. It includes the provision of shelter from unfavourable environmental conditions, feeding, protection from predators, and in some species the training of their offspring as they prepare for adult life. Generally, the more parental care provided, the fewer the number of offspring produced. Certain types of fish produce over 100 million eggs at a spawning. At the other extreme certain mammals, including humans, usually produce only one offspring at a time.

Insects are a group that have successfully colonised the land

During the development of the zygote, an intermediate form, referred to either as the **nymph** or the **larva**, is formed. These are juvenile forms that develop from the egg stage in the life cycle. Insects have a hard outer exoskeleton and in order to grow they have to shed the skin. They do this several times during their development. They are said to undergo an incomplete **metamorphosis**, where the young nymph, which resembles the adult, hatches from the fertilised egg and goes through a series of moults until it reaches full size. An example of an insect exhibiting this type of development is a locust. More advanced insect species develop from a larval stage, which is quite different from the adult. The process involves considerable changes and is called a complete metamorphosis. These insects, such as the housefly and butterfly, also have an additional stage called the pupa or chrysalis. The larva hatches from the egg and is specialised for feeding and growing. The larva undergoes a period of change within the pupa and emerges as the adult that is specialised for dispersal and reproduction.

▶ *Metamorphosis*

Key Terms

Larva (nymph) = the young or immature form of an adult insect.

Metamorphosis = a period of change from the larval stage to the adult.

▼ Study point

It is an advantage to have a pupa stage in the life cycle of an insect for two reasons. It allows the insect to overcome unfavourable conditions as well as enabling the development of a more specialised adult.

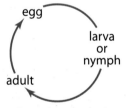

Incomplete metamorphosis

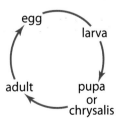

Complete metamorphosis

▼ Study point

The reproduction of flowering plants is studied in detail at A2 level. At AS level details of flower structure or methods of pollination are not required.

More importantly you should concentrate on the link of flowering plants with insects and their similarity to animals in having internal fertilisation. An important evolutionary advance is the seed containing a food store.

Flowering plants have successfully colonised the land

Simple plant forms such as algae, for example seaweeds, are confined to an aquatic environment for at least part, if not all, of their lives. Other plant groups, such as mosses and ferns, are confined to damp areas as the male gametes require a surface film of water in which to swim to the egg. Like the successful land animals, the conifers and flowering plants became independent of water for their reproduction and so were able to colonise the land.

Flowering plants are well suited to life on land because of their method of reproduction and because they have efficient water-carrying xylem vessels, which also function in support. Flowers have pollen grains with a hard coat to withstand desiccation. These contain the male gamete which can be transferred to the female part of the plant. Pollen grains can be transferred by wind or insects.

Plants such as grasses have small, green inconspicuous flowers and the pollen is carried by wind. In plants with brightly coloured flowers and scent for attraction the pollen is carried by insects. The male gamete travels through the tissue of the female part to the egg by means of a pollen tube. This means that sexual reproduction no longer depends on gametes having to travel through a film of water to reach the egg cell. Following fertilisation, the fertilised egg develops into a seed containing a food store.

The flowering plants are the most successful of all terrestrial plants. There are more than 300,000 species. They are found in every type of habitat. A key feature of their success is their relationship with animals, e.g. plants attract animals, particularly insects, to their flowers in order to feed and so exploit their mobility for pollination and seed dispersal. Another important development was the enclosure of the eggs in an ovary and the evolution of the seed. Seeds that result from fertilisation contain food reserves and have a resistant coat and so are able to withstand adverse conditions.

Why did the flowering plants become so successful?

- The interval between flower production and the setting of seed is usually a matter of weeks.

- The production of the seed with a food store enables the embryo to develop until leaves are produced above ground and are able to carry out photosynthesis. The seed also protects the embryo from desiccation and other hazards.

- Generally, leaves are deciduous and succulent and decay rapidly on falling to the ground. This enables humus to be produced and as a consequence the rapid recycling of ions for reuse by plants.

Exam practice questions

Reproductive strategies

1 Some organisms combine cycles of asexual reproduction with periods when they reproduce sexually. The sexual phase is induced when environmental conditions become unfavourable. The diagram shows the life cycle of the water flea, *Daphnia pulex*:

(a) Label points A and B to indicate the type of cell division that takes place. (1)

(b) State whether structures X and Y are haploid or diploid. (1)

(c)(i) Give one potential advantage of reproducing asexually. (1)

(ii) Suggest why organisms such as the water flea are stimulated by certain adverse environmental conditions to enter a sexual phase of reproduction. (2)

(d)(i) Explain what is meant by the term internal fertilisation. (1)

(ii) Give three advantages of internal fertilisation and development to terrestrial animals. (3)

(e) Suggest three reasons why the flowering plants have been so successful in the colonisation of the land. (3)

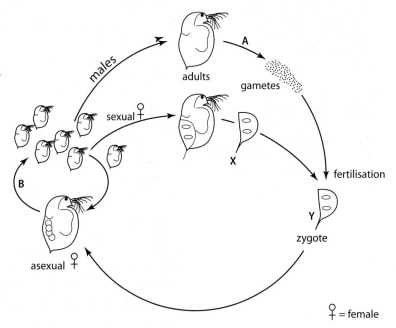

2 The two diagrams show the life cycles of two different groups of insects.

grasshopper

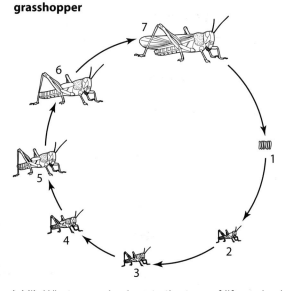

housefly

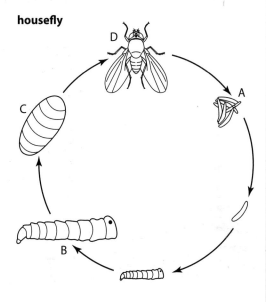

(a)(i) What name is given to the type of life cycle shown by the grasshopper? (1)

(ii) Name the stages labelled 1, 7 and 2–6. (2)

(b)(i) What name is given to the type of life cycle shown by the housefly? (1)

(ii) Name the stages labelled A–D. (2)

3 Using fish and mammals as examples, explain how the reproductive strategies of animals have changed as a result of the evolution of life on land. Comment on the advantages of the mammalian strategies. (10)

BY2

Adaptions for nutrition

Nutrition is the process by which organisms obtain nutrients to provide energy to maintain life functions, and matter to create and maintain structure. Organisms have evolved different methods of obtaining nutrients.

Autotrophic organisms such as green plants use the simple organic materials carbon dioxide and water to manufacture energy-containing complex organic compounds. Heterotrophic organisms depend on autotrophs either directly or indirectly for their food supply. They consume complex organic food material, which must be broken down before it can be used. These organisms use different strategies for obtaining essential nutrients.

By the end of this topic you should be able to:

- Describe the differences between autotrophic and heterotrophic methods of nutrition.

- Describe the different types of heterotrophic organisms.

- Describe the extracellular digestion carried out by saprophytes.

- Distinguish between the processes of ingestion, digestion, absorption and egestion in a human.

- Describe digestion with reference to enzymes which break down carbohydrate, proteins and fats.

- Describe the generalised structure of the human gut.

- Describe the structure and functions of the main parts of the digestive system.

- Describe how the ileum is specialised for absorption.

- Describe the absorption of the products of digestion.

- Describe dentition in a carnivore and grazing herbivore.

- Describe how a herbivore gut is adapted to its diet.

- Compare the gut regions of a herbivore and a ruminant.

- Describe how a parasite is adapted to obtain nourishment from its host.

Methods of nutrition

Autotrophic nutrition

In autotrophic nutrition green plants make their own complex organic molecules from the simple inorganic raw materials, carbon dioxide and water. They do this by the process of photosynthesis using sunlight as an energy source. They provide food for all other life forms and so they are also known as producers. Algae and certain types of bacteria can also photosynthesise using energy from sunlight.

Heterotrophic nutrition

Heterotrophic organisms cannot make their own food. They have to consume complex organic food material produced by autotrophs. Since they eat or consume ready-made food they are known as consumers. All animals are consumers and are dependent on producers for food. Heterotrophs include animals, fungi, some types of protoctists and bacteria.

There are three main forms of heterotrophic nutrition.

Holozoic feeders

These include nearly all animals. They take their food into their bodies and break it down by the process of digestion. Most carry out this process inside the body within a specialised digestive system. The digested material is then absorbed into the body tissues and used by the body cells. Animals that feed solely on plant material are termed herbivores, those that feed on other animals are carnivores, and detritivores are animals that feed on dead and decaying material.

Saprophytes

Saprophytes are also known as saprobionts, and include all fungi and some bacteria. They feed on dead or decaying matter and do not have a specialised digestive system. They feed by secreting enzymes such as proteases, amylases, lipases and cellulases onto the food material outside the body and then absorb the soluble products across the cell membrane by diffusion. This is known as extracellular digestion. Microscopic saprophytes are called decomposers and their activities are important in the decomposition of leaf litter and the recycling of valuable nutrients, such as nitrogen.

YOU SHOULD KNOW ›››

››› that heterotrophs rely directly or indirectly on autotrophs for their food

››› the difference between intracellular and extracellular digestion

››› that saprophytes are important in decomposition and the recycling of nutrients

››› that parasites are highly specialised and the hosts on which they feed suffer some degree of harm

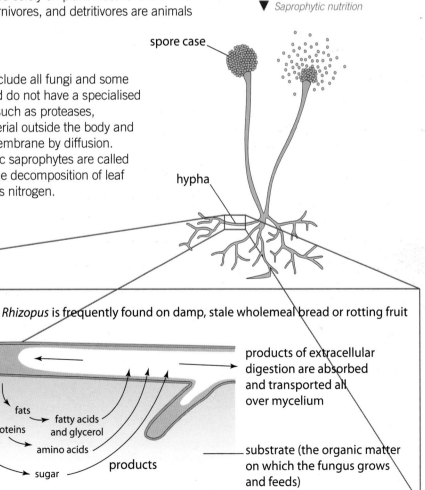

▼ *Saprophytic nutrition*

spore case

hypha

enzymes (e.g. proteases, carbohydrases), produced and secreted from the tip of the hypha, digest the substrate

hypha

Rhizopus is frequently found on damp, stale wholemeal bread or rotting fruit

products of extracellular digestion are absorbed and transported all over mycelium

enzymes

fats → fatty acids and glycerol

proteins

starch → amino acids

sugar

products

substrate (the organic matter on which the fungus grows and feeds)

Key Term

Peristalsis = waves of muscular contraction.

Link The tapeworm on page 139.

32

Knowledge check

Match the terms 1–4 with descriptions A–D.

1. Peristalsis.

2. Digestion.

3. Egestion.

4. Ingestion.

A. Intake of food into the mouth.

B. Alternating contraction and relaxation of gut muscles.

C. The breakdown of large molecules into smaller soluble molecules by means of enzymes.

D. The elimination of indigestible food.

Link Enzymes on page 46.

Parasites

These are organisms that feed on another living organism, referred to as the host. Some parasites live in the body of the host, while others live on the surface. The host always suffers harm to some degree and often death. Parasites are considered to be very highly specialised organisms and show considerable adaptation to their particular way of life. Examples of parasites are the tapeworm, potato blight, caused by a fungus, and *Plasmodium,* the malarial parasite.

Processing food in the digestive system

Organic molecules must be broken down by digestion and absorbed into the body tissues from the digestive system before utilisation in the body cells. Digestion and absorption take place in the gut, which is a long, hollow, muscular tube. The gut is organised to allow movement of its contents in one direction only. In simple organisms, which feed on only one type of food, the gut is undifferentiated. However, in more advanced organisms with a varied diet the gut is divided into various parts along its length and each part is specialised to carry out particular steps in the processes of mechanical and chemical digestion as well as absorption.

The food is processed as it passes along the various regions of the gut. It is propelled along the gut by the **peristalsis**.

muscular wall of oesophagus

circular muscles contra behind the bolus and then relax after the wave of contraction has passed

food bolus

wave of contraction

▲ *Peristalsis*

The human gut performs four main functions:

- Ingestion is the taking in of food into the body through the mouth.

- Digestion is the breakdown of large, insoluble food molecules into simple, soluble molecules by means of enzymes. Mechanical digestion in humans is achieved by the cutting and/or crushing action of the teeth followed by the rhythmical contractions of the gut. The gut wall, particularly the stomach, has layers of muscle to fulfil this function. These are responsible for mixing the food and pushing it along the gut. The physical action also has an important role as it increases the surface area over which enzymes can act. The chemical action of digestion is achieved through the secretion of digestive enzymes.

- Absorption is the passage of digested food through the gut wall into the blood.

- Egestion is the elimination from the body of food that cannot be digested, e.g. cellulose cell walls of plants.

▶ *Functions of the gut*

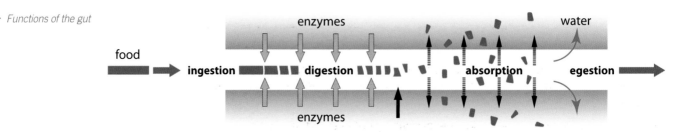

food   ingestion   enzymes   digestion   absorption   water   egestion   enzymes

The human digestive system

Throughout its length from the mouth to the anus the gut wall consists of four tissue layers surrounding a cavity (lumen) of the gut.

- The outer serosa consists of a layer of tough connective tissue that protects the wall of the gut and reduces friction from other organs in the abdomen as the gut moves during the digestive process.

- The muscle layer consists of two layers of muscle running in different directions, the inner circular muscle and the outer longitudinal muscle.

- Collectively these muscles cause waves of muscular contractions, peristalsis, which propels food along the gut. Behind the ball of food the circular muscles contract and the longitudinal muscles relax, thus helping move the food along.

- The sub-mucosa consists of connective tissue containing blood and lymph vessels to take away absorbed food products as well as nerves that co-ordinate the muscular contractions involved in the process of peristalsis.

- The mucosa is the innermost layer and lines the wall of the gut. It secretes mucus, which lubricates and protects the mucosa. In some regions of the gut this layer secretes digestive juices, in others it absorbs digested food.

▼ *General structure of the gut wall*

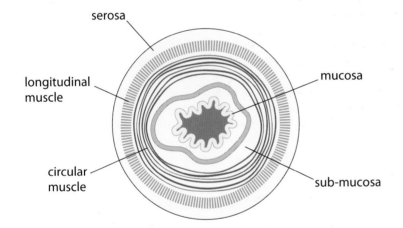

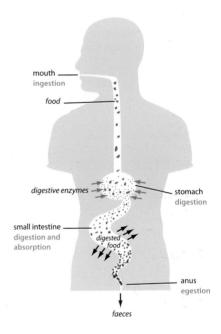

▲ *Simplified structure of gut with functions*

Digestion

The absorption of nutrients by the gut epithelial cells is only possible if the large molecules, carbohydrates, fats and proteins are first broken down or digested into smaller products by means of enzymes. Different enzymes are required to carry out the digestion of the different food substrates and usually more than one type of enzyme is needed for the complete digestion of a particular food.

- Carbohydrates (polysaccharides) are first broken down into disaccharides and then into monosaccharides. The enzyme amylase hydrolyses starch to the disaccharide maltose but another enzyme, maltase, is required to break down the maltose to the monosaccharide, glucose.

- Proteins are broken down into polypeptides, then dipeptides, and finally into amino acids. The general name given to the protein-digesting enzymes is peptidase.

- Proteins are extremely large molecules so endopeptidases hydrolyse peptide bonds within the protein molecule and exopeptidases hydolyse peptide bonds at the ends of these shorter polypeptides.

- Fats are broken down to fatty acids and glycerol by just one enzyme, lipase.

Regional specialisations of the mammalian gut

The mouth

Mechanical digestion begins in the mouth when food is chewed using the teeth. The food is also mixed with saliva from the salivary glands. Saliva is a watery secretion containing mucus and salivary amylase, together with some mineral ions which help to keep the pH in the mouth slightly alkaline, the optimum pH for amylase. Saliva is important for lubricating the food before it is swallowed. Amylase breaks down starch to maltose. After chewing, the ball of food is swallowed and mucus lubricates its passage down the oesophagus.

The stomach

Food enters the stomach and is kept there by the contraction of two rings of muscles, one at the stomach entrance and one at the junction with the duodenum. Food may stay in the stomach for up to four hours and during this time the muscles of the stomach wall contract rhythmically and mix up the food with gastric juice secreted by glands in the stomach wall. Gastric juice contains acid that gives the stomach contents a pH of 2.0. As well as providing the optimum pH for the enzyme, the acid kills most bacteria in the food. Peptidases hydrolyse protein to polypeptides. Mucus is important in forming a lining to protect the stomach wall from the enzymes and acid as well as assisting in the movement of food within the stomach.

▼ **Study point**

Different enzymes have different pH optima so the different enzymes function in particular areas of the gut.

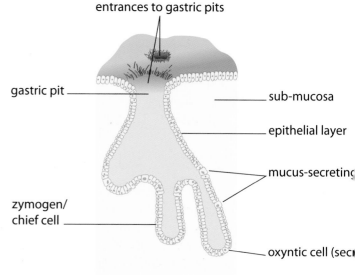

entrances to gastric pits

gastric pit

sub-mucosa

epithelial layer

mucus-secreting

zymogen/ chief cell

oxyntic cell (sec

▲ *Stomach wall*

The small intestine

The small intestine is divided into two regions: the duodenum and the ileum. Relaxation of the muscle at the base of the stomach allows small amounts of the partially digested food into the duodenum a little at a time. The duodenum makes up the first 20 cm of the small intestine and receives secretions from both the liver and the pancreas.

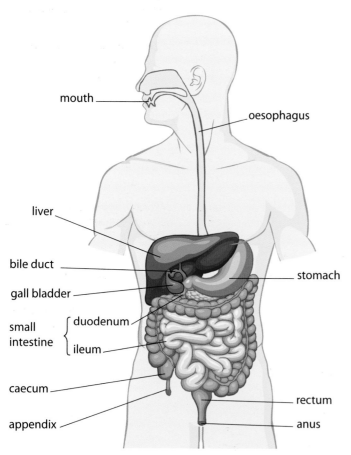

mouth

oesophagus

liver

bile duct

gall bladder

small intestine { duodenum / ileum

stomach

caecum

appendix

rectum

anus

▲ *Structure of human gut*

- Bile is produced in the liver and stored in the gall bladder from where it passes into the duodenum via the bile duct. It contains no enzymes but the bile salts are important in emulsifying the lipids present in the food. Emulsification is achieved by lowering the surface tension of the lipids, causing large globules to break up into tiny droplets. This enables the action of the enzyme lipase to be more efficient as the lipid droplets now have a much larger surface area. Bile also helps to neutralise the acidity of the food as it comes from the stomach.

- The pancreatic juice is secreted from the exocrine glands in the pancreas and enters the duodenum through the pancreatic duct. It contains a number of different enzymes:
  - Endopeptidases, which hydrolyse protein to peptides.
  - Amylase, which breaks down any remaining starch to maltose.
  - Lipase, which hydrolyses lipids into fatty acids and glycerol.

The walls of the duodenum contain glands that secrete an alkaline juice and mucus. The alkaline juice helps to keep the contents of the small intestine at the correct pH for enzyme action, and the mucus is for lubrication and protection.

▼ *Duodenum, gall bladder and liver*

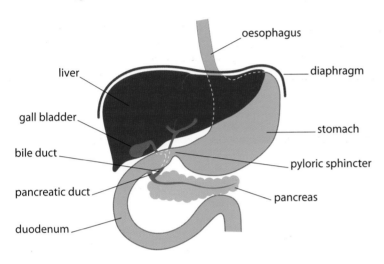

In the small intestine enzymes are secreted by cells at the tips of the finger-like projections called villi.

- Maltase hydrolyses maltose into two glucose molecules.
- Endopeptidases and exopeptidases complete the digestion of polypeptides to amino acids.

The end products of carbohydrate digestion are all monosaccharides. The final stage of carbohydrate digestion is intracellular, as disaccharides are absorbed by the plasma membrane of the epithelial cells before being broken down into monosaccharides.

Absorption

Up to this point the breakdown of carbohydrates, proteins and fats has been considered. The following describes how the soluble products of digestion are absorbed into the body.

The region called the ileum is well adapted for absorption. In humans it is very long and the lining is folded to give a large surface area compared to a smooth tube. On the surface of the villi are epithelial cells with microscopic projections called microvilli. These increase the surface area of the cell membrane of the epithelial cells for absorption.

Absorption takes place mainly in the small intestine. Because energy is required for active absorption, the epithelial cells also contain large numbers of mitochondria.

▼ **Study point**

Highlight each of the three main classes of food and their products in different colours.

33

Knowledge check

Identify the missing word or words.

Saliva, secreted by the •••• ••••, contains the enzyme •••• •••• which begins the breakdown of starch. Disaccharides, such as sucrose, are digested in the small intestine by enzymes secreted by epithelial cells found at the base of the ••••.

Digestion of sucrose results in the formation of the monosaccharides •••• and ••••.

▼ *Endo- and exopeptidase*

endopeptidases hydrolyse peptide bonds within the protein chain, leaving smaller polypeptide sections

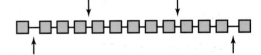

exopeptidases hydrolyse peptide bonds on terminal amino acids

YOU SHOULD KNOW ›››

››› the role of villi and microvilli in absorption

››› how the products of digestion are absorbed in the small intestine

››› the roles of diffusion and active transport in the process

››› the role of the colon in the absorption of water and mineral salts

34

Knowledge check

Identify the missing word or words.

On the surface of villi are epithelial cells with projections called ••••. These increase the •••• •••• for absorption.

Glucose and amino acids are absorbed into the •••• within the villus. Fatty acids and glycerol are absorbed into the •••• •••••.

- Glucose and amino acids are absorbed across the epithelium of the villi by a combination of diffusion and active transport. They pass into the capillary network that supplies each villus. As carbohydrates are being digested continuously there is normally a greater concentration of glucose within the small intestine than in the blood. Glucose therefore diffuses into the blood down a concentration gradient. As glucose is needed for respiration it is continuously being transported in the blood to the cells. As diffusion is a slow process not all the available glucose can be absorbed in this way and some may pass out of the body. However, this does not occur as glucose is also being transported by active transport.

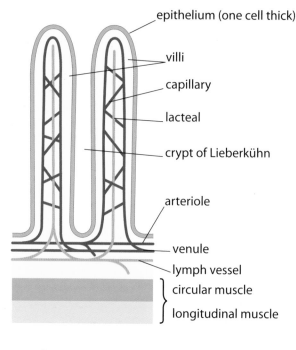

▲ *Small intestine*

- Fatty acids and glycerol are passed into the lacteal. This is a blindly ending lymph capillary found in the centre of each villus. Fatty acids and glycerol are transported in the lymphatic system which ultimately opens into the bloodstream at the thoracic duct.

To summarise, the following methods of transport occur:

- Fatty acids, glycerol and most vitamins pass through the membrane of the epithelial cells by diffusion.

- However, the glucose, amino acids and dipeptides require energy in the form of ATP for absorption by active uptake.

- Dipeptides are then digested intracellularly into simple amino acids.

- Glucose and amino acids then diffuse from the epithelial cell into the blood.

▼ *Epithelial cells of the small intestine*

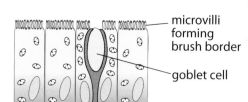

cavity of small intestine

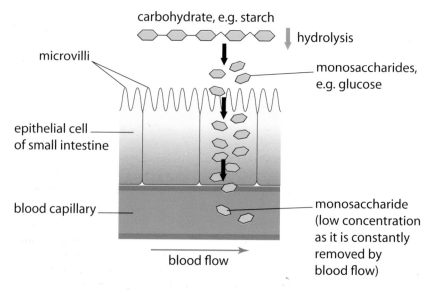

▲ *Absorption*

The large intestine

The large intestine is about 1.5 metres long and is divided into the caecum, the appendix, the colon and the rectum. Water and mineral salts are absorbed from the colon along with vitamins secreted by micro-organisms living in the colon. These bacteria are responsible for making vitamin K and folic acid. By the time it reaches the rectum, indigestible food is in a semi-solid condition. It consists of residues of undigested cellulose, bacteria and sloughed cells and passes along the rectum to be egested as faeces. This process is called defecation.

Fate of digested products after absorption

With the completion of the processes of digestion and absorption the soluble food products are carried in the bloodstream to the tissues for assimilation or to provide energy.

- Glucose is absorbed from the blood by cells, for energy release in respiration.

- Amino acids are absorbed for protein synthesis, the excess cannot be stored so are deaminated whereby the removed amino groups are converted to urea and the remainder to carbohydrate and stored.

- Lipids are used for membranes and hormones, excess are stored as fat.

YOU SHOULD KNOW ›››

››› the structure and functions of the teeth of a carnivore and herbivore

››› the differences between the teeth of a herbivore and a carnivore

››› that ruminants have cellulose-digesting bacteria in their gut and have a modified 'stomach'

Adaptations to different diets

Reptiles and amphibians swallow food whole immediately it is caught, but in mammals food is retained in the mouth whilst it is cut up and chewed. Mammals have a palate that separates the air path (nasal cavity) from the mouth. This allows food to be retained in the mouth rather than swallowed whole between breaths. The gut of a carnivore is short, reflecting the ease with which protein is digested. However, the gut of an herbivore is long because digestion of plant material is difficult.

Since food is retained for cutting, crushing, grinding or shearing according to diet, mammals have evolved different types of teeth with each type being specialised for a different function. Herbivores and carnivores have teeth specialised to suit their diets.

Dentition

Humans have four different types of teeth, incisors, canines, premolars and molars. The teeth are not particularly specialised because humans are omnivores, that is, they eat both plant and animal material. The teeth of herbivores and carnivores are specialised to perform particular functions.

Herbivore dentition

Plant food is a tough material and the teeth of herbivores are modified to ensure that it is thoroughly ground up before it is swallowed. A grazing herbivore, such as a cow or sheep, has incisors on the lower jaw only and cuts against a horny pad on the upper jaw. The canine teeth are indistinguishable from the incisors. A gap, called the diastema, separates the front teeth from the side teeth or premolars. The tongue operates in this gap moving the freshly cut grass to the large grinding surfaces of the cheek teeth. The jaw moves in a circular grinding action in a horizontal plane. The cheek teeth interlock, like the letter W fitting into the letter M. With time the grinding surfaces become worn down, exposing the sharp-edged enamel ridges, which further increases the efficiency of the grinding process. The teeth have open, unrestricted roots so that they can continue to grow throughout the life of the animal.

▼ *Dentition of sheep*

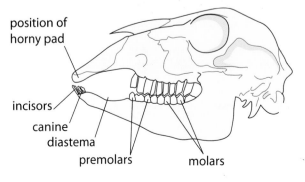

position of horny pad

incisors

canine

diastema

premolars

molars

Key Term

Ruminant = herbivore with a stomach or rumen modified into four chambers.

 35

Knowledge check

Identify the missing word or words.

The jaws of a carnivore move vertically whereas the jaws of a herbivore move from •••• •••• •••• .

There are no upper incisors in the sheep instead there is a •••• •••• on which the incisors of the lower jaw cut vegetation. The herbivore has a gap called a •••• separating the front teeth from the side teeth. The carnivore has a pair of large specialised teeth called •••• which slide past each other to tear flesh from the bones of its prey.

▼ Study point

Herbivorous mammals do not produce cellulase enzymes. In non-ruminant animals such as the rabbit and horse cellulase-secreting bacteria live in the caecum but in ruminants the bacteria live in the specialised stomach which has four chambers.

▼ Study point

The gut of a carnivore is short, reflecting the ease with which protein is digested. The gut of an herbivore is long, reflecting the difficulty in digesting plant material.

▼ Study point

It is often useful to summarise a passage that you have read. For example, the gut region of a ruminant is adapted to its diet by having a long gut, containing cellulose-digesting bacteria and being able to regurgitate its food and 'chew the cud'.

Carnivore dentition

Carnivorous mammals, such as a tiger, have teeth adapted for catching and killing prey, cutting or crushing bones and for tearing meat. The sharp incisors grip and tear flesh from bone. The canine teeth are large, curved and pointed for seizing prey, for killing and also tearing flesh. The premolars and molars are for cutting and crushing. Carnivores have a pair of specialised cheek teeth, called carnassials, which slide past each other like the blades of gardening shears. The jaw muscles are well developed and powerful to enable the carnivore to grip the prey firmly and help in crushing bone. There is no side-to-side movement of the jaw, found only in herbivores, as this would lead to the jaw being dislocated when dealing with prey. The vertical jaw movement is greater than in herbivores allowing the jaw to open widely for capturing and killing prey.

▶ *Dentition of dog*

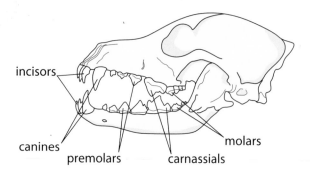

Ruminants

Animals produce 35% of all the protein eaten by humans. Of this, nearly half comes from **ruminants**, such as cows and sheep, which eat mainly grass and forage, a large proportion of which consists of cellulose cell walls.

Mutualism or symbiosis involves a close association between members of two different species and where both organisms derive some benefit from the relationship. Herbivorous mammals, such as cows and sheep, lack the ability to produce cellulase enzymes and so cannot digest cellulose. A large proportion of plant material consists of cellulose cell walls. Certain herbivores, e.g. cows, have formed an association with cellulose-digesting bacteria which live in the gut of the cow. In this association the mammal acquires the products of cellulose digestion and the bacteria receive a constant supply of food and can grow in a suitable sheltered environment.

The cow provides a region of the gut for the bacteria to inhabit and in return the bacteria digest the cellulose for the cow. However, the region of the gut must be kept separate from the main digestive region so that:

- Food can be kept there long enough for the bacteria to carry out the digestion of the cellulose.

- The bacteria are isolated from the mammal's own digestive juices so that they are in the optimum pH for their activities and they are not killed by extremes of pH.

Ruminants have a 'stomach' that is made up of four chambers. Three of the chambers are derived from the lower part of the oesophagus and one chamber is the true stomach.

▶ *Ruminant gut*

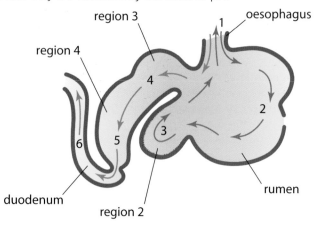

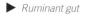

Cellulose digestion takes place as follows:

- The grass is chopped by the teeth, mixed with saliva, and the cud formed is swallowed and passes to the rumen.

- In the rumen is the first chamber where the food is mixed with cellulose-digesting bacteria to produce glucose. This is fermented to form organic acids that are absorbed into the blood, and provides energy for the cow. The waste products are carbon dioxide and methane that are passed out.

- The fermented grass passes to the next chamber and is formed into cud, which is regurgitated into the mouth for further chewing.

- The cud passes directly into the third chamber where water is reabsorbed.

- The fourth and last chamber functions as a 'normal' stomach and protein is digested.

- The digested food passes to the next region, the small intestine, where the products of digestion are absorbed.

Parasites

Parasites are organisms that live on or in another organism, called the host, and obtain nourishment at the expense of the host. Parasites therefore cause harm to some degree and often cause death. Many organisms are parasitised for at least part of their lives. Plants are parasitised by bacteria, fungi, viruses, nematodes and insects; animals are parasitised by bacteria, fungi, viruses, proctista, tapeworms, nematodes, insects and mites. Even bacteria are parasitised by viruses called bacteriophages! The study of parasites is of economic importance as they cause disease in humans, crops and domesticated animals.

Pork tapeworm – a parasite of the gut

All animals have a struggle to survive, to avoid competition with others and to avoid being preyed upon by other animals. Parasites have become specialised and undergone considerable evolutionary changes in order to survive in the host. The gut parasite (*Taenia solium*) is a particularly good example.

Imagine living in the gut of another animal! The tapeworm is ribbon-like and can be up to 10 metres long! It has a 'head' made up of muscle on which are suckers and hooks. Its body consists of a linear series of thin segments. The pork tapeworm has two hosts. The primary host is the human and the pig is the secondary host. The pig becomes infected if it feeds in drainage channels contaminated by human faeces. Humans are infected by eating undercooked infected pork.

▶ *Tapeworm*

▼ **Study point**

A detailed knowledge of the life cycle is not required.

▼ **Study point**

The tapeworm does not have a gut. This is because it is surrounded by the host's nutrients, which are absorbed through the body surface.

139

36

The pork tapeworm lives in the gut of its host. It has two hosts. The primary host is the ···· and the ···· is the secondary host. It has no need for many organ systems but has a highly developed ···· system. It has suckers and ···· for attachment to the gut wall. It also has a thick ···· to prevent digestion by the enzymes of the host. It has a very thin body and so has a large ···· ···· to absorb the digested food of its host.

▼ Study point

The tapeworm is hermaphrodite, that is, both sex organs are present in the one individual. The gut could not accommodate two tapeworms so mating would be impossible. It therefore fertilises its own eggs.

Although the tapeworm lives in an immediate source of food, it needs to survive the hostile conditions found in the gut. The following are the problems that the gut parasite has to overcome in order to survive:

- It lives surrounded by digestive juices and mucus.

- Food, mixed with digestive juices, is in constant motion as it is churned about as well as being propelled along the length of the gut by peristaltic contractions of the muscular wall.

- It lives in extremes conditions of pH along the length of the gut.

- The immune system of the host.

- If the host dies then so does the parasite.

In order to survive the hostile environment the tapeworm must:

- Have a means of penetrating the host.

- Have a means of attachment to the host.

- Protect itself against the immune responses of the host.

- Develop only those organs that are essential for survival.

- Produce many eggs.

- Have an intermediate host.

- Have resistant stages to overcome the period away from a host.

The tapeworm has evolved the following structural modifications to enable it to live as a parasite:

- Suckers and a double row of curved hooks for attachment to the wall of the gut.

- A body covering which protects it from the host's immune responses.

- A thick cuticle and the production of inhibitory substances on the surface of the segments to prevent its digestion by the host's enzymes.

- Because tapeworms live in a stable environment they do not need to move around and do not require a sensory system. This has led to the degeneration of unnecessary organs. They do have simple excretory and nervous systems but most of the body is concerned with reproduction.

- The tapeworm is very thin and has a large surface area to volume ratio. It is surrounded by digested food so it has a very simple digestive system and pre-digested food can be absorbed over the entire body surface.

- Because the gut could not accommodate two tapeworms, each segment contains both male and female reproductive organs. Vast numbers of eggs are produced, with each mature segment containing up to 40,000 eggs. The mature segments pass out of the host's body with the faeces.

- The eggs have resistant shells and can survive until eaten by the secondary host. Further development can then take place and the embryos which hatch from the eggs move into the muscles of the pig and remain dormant until the meat of the pig is eaten by a human.

Harmful effects of the pork tapeworm

The adult worms cause little discomfort but, if the eggs are eaten by humans, dormant embryos form cysts in various organs and damage the surrounding tissue. Adults can be treated with appropriate drugs. Public health measures and frequent inspection of meat are essential measures.

Adaptions for nutrition

1   The diagram represents the human digestive system.

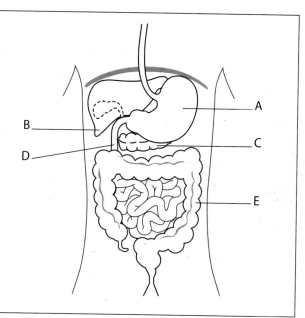

(a)   Using the appropriate letters shown on the diagram match the following statements. (4)

An acidic region.

The region where the hydrolysis of protein begins.

The region where the enzyme amylase is produced.

The structure which produces chemicals which emulsify fats.

(b)   In the villi of the small intestine what is the function of:

(i) the lacteal (1)

(ii) the capillaries (1)

(c)   Apart from its length, state two other ways in which the surface area of the small intestine is increased. (2)

---

2   The diagram shows the processes that would take place in a simple tube gut.

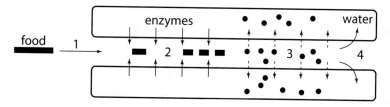

(a)(i) Name the processes numbered 1–4. (2)

(ii) Define the process number 3. (1)

(b)(i) Explain why the digestion of proteins is more efficient if they are exposed to endopeptidases before being acted upon by exopeptidases. (2)

(ii) The figure below shows a peptide. Each circled letter represents a single amino acid. (2)

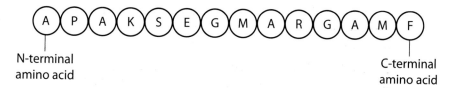

N-terminal
amino acid

C-terminal
amino acid

This peptide was digested first with endopeptidase and then with an exopeptidase. Endopeptidase hydrolyses peptide bonds on the C-terminal side of either the amino acid R or the amino acid K. Exopeptidase hydrolyses one amino acid at a time from the C-terminal end of a peptide, but will not hydrolyse a dipeptide.

Using the instructions above, show the two steps whereby the peptide is broken down by endopeptidase and then by exopeptidase to give dipeptides and free amino acids.

3 The diagram shows the arrangement of layers in a gut wall.

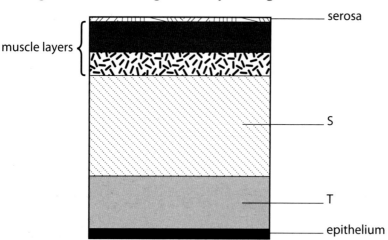

(a) How does the arrangement of fibres differ in the two muscle layers? (1)

(b) What term is used for the process by which the muscle layers push food along the gut? (1)

(c) Label layers S and T. (1)

(d) Name two structures found in layer S and give their functions in nutrition. (4)

4 The drawings show the skulls of two mammals.

P 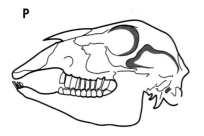   Q

(a)(i) Identify the type of nutrition for each animal. (1)

 (ii) For each animal, describe one adaptation of its dentition to its diet. (2)

 (iii) Explain why the gut of Q is much shorter than that of P. (1)

(b)(i) Describe how the stomach of mammal P is adapted to its diet. (4)

 (ii) Suggest why mammal Q has a large stomach, even though the remainder of its gut is reduced. (1)

5 (a) Define the term parasite. (2)

(b) The tapeworm, *Taenia solium*, is a parasite of humans. Its life cycle includes a secondary host.

 (i) Name the secondary host. (1)

 (ii) Describe how the parasite is transmitted from a human to its secondary host. (1)

 (iii) Explain how humans may become infected with the tapeworm. (1)

(c) *Taenia* is a parasite which lives in the human digestive tract or gut.

 (i) State one adaptation of *Taenia* which ensures that it stays in place in the gut of the host. (1)

 (ii) Explain why *Taenia* is not destroyed by the secretions of the human host. (2)

(d) *Taenia* has a very high rate of reproduction. Explain how this is advantageous to the parasite. (1)

Exam practice answers

1

Feature	Carbohydrate	Lipid	Protein
Can be saturated or unsaturated		✓	
Contains peptide bonds			✓
Contains the elements carbon, hydrogen and oxygen	✓	✓	✓
Can contain disulphide bonds			✓
Cellulose and glucose are examples	✓		

2 (a) (i) Hexose   (ii) Maltose   (iii) Water   (iv) 1 and 4

(b) (i) The positions of –OH and –H are reversed on C1.

(ii) Molecules which differ in structure but have the same general formula.

(c) β glucose

(d) Long chains strengthened by cross-linkages/microfibrils.

(e) Cellulose cell walls confer strength/rigidity/structural support.

3 (a) (i) Glycerol

(ii) The elimination of water/condensation reaction.

(iii) A long chain (16+) of hydrocarbon atoms/long chain of CH_2 groups.

(b) (i) R in fat is saturated/no double bonds between carbon atoms.
R in oil is unsaturated/has double bonds.

(ii) Storage of energy.

(iii) Lipid yields twice as much energy as the same mass of carbohydrate.

4 (a)

	Triglyceride	Phospholipid
Structural difference 1	3 fatty acids	2 fatty acids
Structural difference 2	Glycerol head only	Glycerol + phosphate head
Where compound is found in organisms	Under skin/around body organs/nerve cells/seeds	Cell membranes

(b) Stearic/saturated has more H or converse.
Stearic has no double bonds in hydrocarbon chain or converse.
Stearic acid is a straight hydrocarbon chain or converse.

(c) Stearic acid/saturated fatty acid.

5 (a) (i) A – phosphate; B – glycerol; C – fatty acid

(ii) Ester bond; a condensation reaction; elimination of water molecule.

(iii) Plasma/cell membrane.

(b) Phospholipid has two fatty acid chains, whereas there are three in a triglyceride;
no phosphate group in triglyceride but present in phospholipid.

6 (a) (i) A – amino acid; B – triglyceride

(ii) Nitrogen; sulphur

(b) Condensation; peptide

(c) (i) Add Biuret to test solution, blue colour changes to mauve/purple colour if positive result.

(ii) Colour change may be masked.

7 (a)

Level of protein structure	Types of bonds			
	Peptide	Hydrogen	Disulphide	Ionic
Primary	✓			
Secondary	✓	✓		
Tertiary	✓	✓	✓	✓

(b) (i) Two or more polypeptide chains present.

(ii) Haemoglobin

8 (a) (i) Dipeptide   (ii) Peptide   (Iii) Hydrolysis

(b) Different R groups

(c) 20

9 (a) A – hydrogen; B – disulphide bridge; C – ionic

(b) (i) α helix

(ii) Hydrogen bonds

(iii) β pleated sheet

(c) Tertiary

(d) (i) β glucose

(ii) Long, parallel chains cross-linked between the chains to form microfibrils. It gives strength.

10 Magnesium – component of chlorophyll.
Iron – component of haemoglobin.
Phosphate – component of nucleic acids/membrane/phospholipids.
Calcium – deposited in bones and teeth.

11 This essay requires any 10 of the 15 points available.

Structure

Consists of elements carbon, hydrogen and oxygen; glycerol + 3 fatty acids; joined by condensation reactions; formation of ester bonds; there are saturated and unsaturated fatty acids; phosphate group replaces one fatty acid in phospholipids.

Functions

Energy storage; releases more energy per unit mass than carbohydrates; makes seeds lighter/smaller for dispersal/energy store for hibernation; phospholipid component of cell membrane; controls entry of molecules into cell; insulation; protection of internal organs; buoyancy for aquatic animals; waterproofing/myelin sheath, etc.

BY1: Cell structure and organisation

1 (a)

Feature	Prokaryotic cell	Eukaryotic plant cell
Chromosomes		✓
Respiration in mesosomes	✓	
Membrane-bound organelles		✓
Ribosomes present	✓	✓

(b)

Prokaryote	**Eukaryote**
Ribosomes small	Larger ribosomes
Murein cell wall	Cellulose cell wall

2

Structural feature	Plant cells	Bacteria	Viruses
May contain mitochondria	✓		
Have cell walls	✓	✓	
May contain DNA	✓	✓	✓
May contain chloroplasts	✓		
Do not have a membrane-bound nucleus		✓	✓
May have plasmids		✓	

3 (a) (i) A – cell wall; B – chloroplast; C – plasmodesmata/pore; D – vacuole; E – rough endoplasmic reticulum/ribosome

   (ii) A – support/stop cell bursting/protection; C – movement of materials from cell to cell; E – protein synthesis

(b) (i) Cellulose

   (ii) Starch

   (iii) Ribose

(c) Plant has cell wall, chloroplast and large permanent vacuole, animal cell does not.

4 (a)

Feature	Bacterial cell	Leaf cell	Muscle cell
Cell wall	✓	✓	✗
Large permanent vacuole	✗	✓	✗
Nuclear membrane	✗	✓	✓
Chloroplasts	✗	✓	✗
Mesosomes	✓	✗	✗
Mitochondria	✗	✓	✓

(b) (i) A number of similar cells, carrying out a common function.

   (ii) Muscle

5 (a) A – granum; B – stroma; C – double membrane/envelope; D – thylakoid

(b) Chlorophyll

6 (a) A – matrix; B – crista/internal membrane

(b) E – site of protein synthesis; polypeptide chains built up at ribosome; transport polypeptides/proteins; ribosomes read genetic code.

   F – buds of vesicles/package proteins into vesicles; these contain molecules for secretion; transport protein

molecules to cell membrane; synthesis of glycoproteins/ modification of proteins.

(c) Metabolically active/secretory cell involved in active processes; ATP/energy dependent; ATP manufactured by mitochondrion; hormone synthesis requires ATP.

(d) Cut in different plane.

7 (a) RNA/ribosomal RNA; protein

(b) Rough endoplasmic reticulum

(c) Protein synthesis

(d) Nucleolus

8

Statement	Smooth endoplasmic reticulum	Mitochondria	Golgi body	Rough endoplasmic reticulum
Surrounded by a double membrane		✓		
Produces glycoprotein			✓	
Buds off lysosomes			✓	
Manufactures enzymes				✓
Most abundant at sites of active transport		✓		
Abundant in cells secreting lipids	✓			
Closely associated with ribosomes				✓

9 This essay requires any 10 of the 15 points available.

RER

System of flattened sacs or cisternae; with ribosomes attached; the site of protein synthesis; continuous with nuclear membrane.

Golgi

Interconnected flattened sacs; proteins from RER are transported in vesicles; vesicles fuse with Golgi membrane and contents are shed into Golgi sacs; contents are packaged into more complex molecules such as enzymes/glycoproteins; another function such as transporting or storing lipids; at the other end of the Golgi body vesicles containing product are budded off; and move to plasma membrane with which they fuse; exocytosis of contents.

Lysosomes

Membrane-bound sacs or vesicles which contain digestive enzymes; vesicles fuse with membrane of cell vacuoles and enzymes digest contents; which have been previously enclosed by phagocytosis; enzymes in lysosomes also break down worn out organelles/autolysis.

BY1: Cell membrane and transport

1 (a) (i) Fluid mosaic model; a mosaic of protein molecules/ irregularly or randomly arranged with a fluid/moving lipid layer.

(ii) A – phospholipid bilayer/fatty acid tails; B – extrinsic protein; C – transmembrane/ carrier/intrinsic protein.

(iii) Allows the passage of polar/charged/ionic/hydrophilic molecules/facilitated diffusion.

(b) Movement against a concentration gradient; requires energy/ATP.

(c) Providing structural support; allowing transport across the membrane; recognition sites/glycoproteins.

2

Type of compound	Method of transport into cell	Component of the membrane through which it passes	Factor affecting rate of transport
Lipid soluble	Diffusion	Lipid bilayer	Size of molecules
Water soluble in high external concentration	Facilitated diffusion	Protein channel/ carrier	Cell concentration Size of molecules
Water soluble in very low external concentration	Active transport	Carrier proteins	Respiration rate ATP production

3 Process A – diffusion; as the concentration difference increases, the rate of uptake increases; not affected by respiratory inhibitors; no ATP required/passive.

Process B – facilitated diffusion; at higher concentration differences rate of uptake slows down/plateau levels out; transport/carrier/channel proteins full; not affected by respiratory inhibitors; no ATP required/passive.

Process C – active transport; rate slows down; saturation of protein carriers; slowed by respiratory inhibitors; process needs ATP/it is an active process.

4

Statement	Diffusion	Facilitated diffusion	Active transport
Substance dissolves in lipid part of membrane.	✓		
Will not take place in the presence of cyanide.			✓
Movement involves membrane proteins.		✓	✓
Does not require cell energy.	✓	✓	
Rate is proportional to concentration gradient across membrane.	✓		
Due to random movement of molecules in external solution.	✓	✓	
Membrane proteins act as pumps.			✓

5 (a) Water potential is the capacity of water to leave or enter a system or cell.

(b)(i) J – plasma/cell membrane; K – cell wall

(ii) The cell is plasmolysed/cell membrane has just pulled away from the cell wall.

(iii) Cell wall is permeable; sucrose diffused/moved through to T; there must be the same concentration of solution on both sides of the wall.

6 (a) $\Psi = +1000 - 1800 = -800\,\text{kPa}$

(b) Plasmolysed; cell in low water potential solution; water passes out of cell; cytoplasm/vacuole shrinks.

(c) Wilts

(d) Incipient plasmolysis

(e) Water passes in and cell bursts

7 This essay requires any 10 of the 15 points available.

(Any 4 points from the following)

The membrane consists of a phospholipid bilayer; with hydrophilic phosphate heads and hydrophobic lipid tails; intrinsic/transmembrane/carrier/channel proteins and extrinsic proteins; glycoproteins on surface/cholesterol in membrane; reference to fluid mosaic model.

(Any 6 points from the following)

Diffusion from a high external to a low internal concentration; only lipid soluble molecules can pass through phospholipid layer; other small molecules can diffuse through intrinsic protein channels; by means of facilitated diffusion; proteins can also act as carriers; a molecule may be picked up and the protein configuration is changed and ejects molecule on other side of membrane; this is active transport against the concentration gradient; this requires energy/ATP; water molecules enter by osmosis along a water potential gradient.

BY2: Biodiversity and evolution

1 (a) species (b) evolution (c) biodiversity (d) binomial
   (e) taxonomy.

2

	Plantae	Animalia	Protoctista	Fungi	Prokaryotae
Jellyfish		✓			
Yeast				✓	
Amoeba			✓		
Fern	✓				
Bacterium					✓

3 (a)

Kingdom	Phylum	Features of phylum	Class	Example
Animalia	Annelida	Segmented body; fluid-filled body cavity; thin permeable skin; closed circulatory system (any 2)	Polychaeta	Lugworm *Arenicola marina*
Animalia	Chordata	Soft moist skin Aquatic larva with gills; Adults with simple lungs	Amphibia	Common frog *Rana temporaria*
Animalia	Arthropoda	Body divided into segments; body divided into head, thorax and abdomen; hard exoskeleton; jointed legs (any 2)	Insecta	Desert locust *Schistocerca gregaria*
Fungi	Basidio-mycota	Hyphae; cell wall of chitin; reproduce using spores	Basiiomyctes	Field mushroom *Agaricus campestris*

(b) *Schistocerca*

4 (a) 6
  (b) *Macroderma gigas*

5 (a) Adaptive radiation.
  (b) No competition (from other birds); vacant niches; subsequent intraspecific competition. (Any 2 points)
  (c) Unable to interbreed to produce fertile offspring.

6 (a) Phylum Chordata; class Mammalia; genus *Acinonyx*.
  (b) Phylum – vertebral column or backbone/well-developed brain/CNS enclosed in a cranium.
     Class – endothermic/lungs/hair or fur/sweat glands/feed young on milk.
  (c) (i) DNA fingerprinting/DNA hybridisation/protein sequencing.
     (ii) The DNA sequence of bases shared between individuals is very high/a close match.

7 (a) Segmented body; jointed limbs.
  (b) Advantage – waterproof; disadvantage – limits growth/necessitates moulting (ecdysis).
  (c) Class.

BY2: Adaptations for gaseous exchange

1 (a) The movement of molecules/particles from a region of high concentration to a region of lower concentration/along a concentration gradient from high to low.
  (b) *Amoeba* – being unicellular it has a large surface area to volume ratio/gases have a short diffusion path.
     Planaria – although multicellular, these are flat and so have a large surface area to volume ratio.
  (c) (i) Doubling the length results in halving the ratio/the size of the ratio is inversely proportional to the length.
     (ii) I. Alveoli.
        II. As the mammal is large, it has a small surface area to volume ratio; therefore diffusion paths are long/diffusion is slow; alveoli are needed to increase surface area.

2 (a) (i) Large surface area/thin or short diffusion path/good blood supply/permeable to gases.
     (ii) Infolding reduces heat loss/water loss; protection by ribs.
  (b) (i) To move the respiratory medium over the respiratory surface; to maintain the concentration gradient.
     (ii) Diaphragm; intercostal muscles.

3 (a) A: cartilage; B: bronchiole; C: alveoli; D: diaphragm.
  (b) A: To provide flexible support to trachea/prevents collapse of air passage.
     C: Gas exchange surface.
     D: Lowered by muscles to increase volume of thorax.

4 (a) (i) Where the trachiole touches the muscle.
     (ii) Oxygen is supplied directly to the tissues so no transport system or pigment is required. This makes for a much faster system.
     (iii) $\dfrac{\text{Difference}}{\text{Original}} \times 100 = \dfrac{0.032}{0.064} \times 100 = 50\%$
  (b) Intercostal muscles contract; ribs move up and out; diaphragm contracts/flattens; volume increases; pressure decreases; air rushes in as atmospheric pressure is higher.

5 (a) Water contains less oxygen than air; diffusion rates are much slower; water is a dense medium making it more difficult to pump.
  (b) Parallel flow – water and blood in gills flow in the same direction.
     Counter-current – water and blood flow in opposite directions.
     Concentration gradient is maintained over the entire distance travelled by water over the gills, making it more efficient.

6 A: Cuticle; reduces water loss.
   B: Palisade mesophyll layer: main site of photosynthesis.
   C: Air spaces: for diffusion of gases.
   D: Stomata/stoma: for exchange of gases.

7 (a) A: guard cells; B: epidermal cells/epidermis.

(b) Allow gas exchange/allow oxygen and carbon dioxide to enter and leave the leaf; control water loss.

(c) Potassium ions are pumped/active transport into the guard cells/malate production by chloroplasts; the water potential is lowered; water flows in by osmosis; guard cells become turgid; inner wall of guard cell is thicker than outer wall; so guard cells curve away from each other.

(d) Cyanide inhibits respiration/ATP synthesis; stops active transport of potassium into guard cell.

8 This essay requires any 10 of the 15 points available.

Leaf is flat and thin/large surface area to volume ratio; large surface area to trap light; thin to give a short diffusion path; outer epidermal layer covered by cuticle; reduces water loss; palisade mesophyll consisting of vertically arranged packed cells; to give maximum light absorption; spongy mesophyll with large intercellular spaces; enabling passage of respiratory gases and water vapour; movement of gases in and out of leaf through stomata; stomata consist of pore surrounded by two guard cells; change in water potential causes guard cells to open stomata; stomata open during daylight hours and closure at other times prevents water loss.

BY2: Transport in animals and plants

1 (a) Arteries – small lumen vein – wider lumen; thick muscle wall;– thin muscle wall; regular shape – irregular shape.

(b)(i) Blood tries to flow back; and fills pockets which forces the valve to close.

(ii) There is no backflow as the veins are located above the heart; blood moves by gravity.

(iii) Veins lie next to/in muscle; when muscle contracts the vein is squeezed; this forces the blood towards the heart.

(c)(i) No nucleus; allows more space for haemoglobin; oxygen combines with haemoglobin to form oxyhaemoglobin.

Red blood cells have a large surface area due to biconcave shape.

Has a flexible/elastic membrane, allowing greater contact with capillary walls.

(ii) To carry carbon dioxide.

2 (a) Separate circulation for body and lungs; blood passes through heart twice in one circuit; separates oxygenated and deoxygenated blood; maintains high blood pressure and greater oxygen concentration to the tissues; lower pressure for pulmonary circulation.

(b)

Blood vessel	Carries blood from	Carries blood to	Blood is oxygenated/ deoxygenated	Pressure is high/low
Aorta	Left ventricle	Body/ tissues	Oxygenated	High
Vena cava	Body/ tissues	Right atrium	Deoxygenated	Low
Pulmonary artery	Right ventricle	Lungs	Deoxygenated	High
Pulmonary vein	Lungs	Left atrium	Oxygenated	Low

(c) Site of exchange; removes waste products between blood and tissues; tissue fluid formation; slows blood flow to allow time for diffusion; reduces blood pressure/carries blood at low pressure.

3 (a) Artery

(b) 5 ± 0.5 kPa

(c) Contraction of ventricle/ventricular systole

(d) Ventricle relaxes/diastole.

(e) Further away from the heart; friction/more resistance.

4 (a) The semi-lunar valve closes so preventing the backflow of blood into the ventricle; the left ventricle relaxes/diastole.

(b) One heartbeat takes 0.8 seconds

$$\frac{60 \text{ seconds}}{0.8} = 75 \text{ beats per minute}$$

(c) The thickness of the muscular wall affects the pressure; the left atrium forces blood into the ventricle which is close to it; the left ventricle has to push blood around the entire body which is further; the right ventricle has to push blood to the lungs which are closer and need a lower blood pressure.

5 (a)(i) As the partial pressure of oxygen going into the tissues decreases, more oxygen is released/dissociated.

(ii) The haemoglobin is fully saturated at relatively low partial pressures of oxygen.

(b)(i) The curved line to the right-hand side of curve A.

(ii) Bohr effect.

(c)(i) A curve to the left of curve A means that the haemoglobin more readily combines/has a greater affinity for oxygen at lower partial pressures.

(ii) It lives under low oxygen conditions.

6 (a)(i) The left ventricle has a thicker muscular wall/contracts with more force.

(ii) Pressure is greater in the atria/lower in ventricles; atrio-ventricular valves are open.

(b) X: atrioventricular node; Y: bundle of His/Purkinje tissue.

(c)(i) The delay allows blood to pass into the ventricles from the atria/so that atria can empty; before the ventricles contract (this prevents the ventricles contracting before the atria are emptied).

(ii) So that the ventricles contract from the base upwards; so more blood is forced out/ventricles empty completely.

(d) If heart muscle at S was affected there would be no contraction but if muscle at T was affected there would be some contraction although resulting in a reduced force.

7 (a) A: Xylem vessel – transports water/mineral salts.

B: Sieve tube – transports organic materials/sucrose/amino acids.

C: Companion cell – releases energy as ATP/makes proteins.

(b) Supports/strengthens/prevents vessel collapsing/adhesion of water, aids movement of water upwards.

8 (a) Cohesion is the strong attraction that water molecules exert on one another.

(b) Water molecules evaporating through the stomata at the top of the column are replaced from below; and because of cohesion this creates an upward force (tension) throughout the whole column.

(c) Adhesion between the water molecules and the xylem wall.

(d)(i) Root pressure.

(ii) The active transport of ions into the xylem of the root; creates an osmotic gradient/water is drawn in at the base of the xylem.

9 (a)(i) Xerophyte.

(ii) Sunken stomata – water vapour held above stomata.

Hairs surrounding stomata – helps to retain water vapour.

Thick cuticle reduces water loss.

(b)(i) Hydrophyte.

(ii) Large air spaces – for buoyancy/diffusion.

Stomata on upper surface – to allow gas exchange with the air.

Thin cuticle – as little water vapour loss.

Little support tissue/xylem – as buoyed by water.

10 (a) Sucrose.

(b) The C^{14} is taken into the leaf half way up the stem; and appears at the top and in the roots.

(c)(i) The top of the stem is the growing point where carbohydrate is needed; to provide ATP for respiration.

(ii) Sinks.

11. This essay should include 10 out of 15 points.

Xylem transports water and mineral salts from roots to leaves; phloem transports sucrose and amino acids from source to sink; from leaves to other parts of the plant; xylem is made of vessels and tracheids; during development xylem vessels lose their end walls and form continuous tubes; their wall is lignified to strengthen; mature xylem vessels are dead; phloem is made of sieve tubes and companion cells; the sieve tubes lose most of their organelles but remain alive; they have perforated sieve plates that allow solutes to pass through; sucrose/solutes flow in both directions; companion cells contain organelles/mitochondria and provide ATP for sieve tubes; flow of water up the xylem by cohesion tension theory and capillarity; in phloem there is a mass flow but may involve cytoplasmic streaming/protein filaments.

BY2: Reproductive strategies

1 (a) A: meiosis; B: mitosis.

(b) X: haploid; Y: diploid.

(c)(i) Allows a rapid increase in numbers, where environment is stable.

(ii) Offspring need to adapt to new conditions in order to survive and sexual reproduction leads to variation.

(d)(i) The fusion of gametes/sperm and eggs by the use of an intromittent organ.

(ii) More chance of gametes meeting and therefore less are wasted; gametes become independent of water/gametes do not dehydrate; fertilised eggs develop inside the body of the female.

(e) Rapid life cycle; food store in seed allows rapid growth of embryo; food store enables seed to survive for long periods/dormancy; seed protected by resistant outer layer/seed coat; leaf fall allows recycling of nutrients; no need for water for fertilisation; pollination by wind or animals; dispersal; large numbers of seeds produced.

2 (a)(i) Incomplete metamorphosis.

(ii) 1: egg; 7: adult/imago; 2–6: nymphs/instar

(b)(i) Complete metamorphosis.

(ii) A: egg; B: larva; C: pupa; D: adult/imago.

3 This essay requires any 10 from 15 points.

In fish, gametes are shed into the water; fertilisation is external; many gametes fail to fuse and are wasted; embryo entirely dependent on yolk supply for development; many embryos wasted due to predation, etc.; finding suitable conditions for development is a random process.

In terrestrial mammals there is internal fertilisation; gametes fuse independently of water since they are placed inside the female; so there is a greater certainty of fertilisation; the number of eggs is much reduced; the internally developing embryo not dependent solely on yolk but fed via placenta; high level of protection from external hazards; more time/energy/resources available as there are fewer offspring; there are varying degrees of parental care; dens, burrows, sites for protection from predation.

BY2: Adaptions for nutrition

1 (a) Acidic – A; protein hydrolysis – A; amylase produced – C; produces bile – B.

(b)(i) Lacteal absorbs fatty acids and glycerol.

(ii) Capillaries absorb glucose and amino acids.

(c) Folded; numerous villi; microvilli.

2 (a)(i) 1: ingestion; 2: digestion; 3: absorption; 4: egestion.

(ii) The passage of digested food through the intestine/gut wall into the blood stream.

(b)(i) Endopeptidase cuts in the middle of the chain/produces several smaller chains; producing many ends for exopeptidase to act upon.

(ii) APAK+SEGMAR+GAMF
AP+A+K+SE+G+M+A+R+GA+M+F

3 (a) One layer has fibres arranged longitudinally, one has circular fibres.

(b) Peristalsis.

(c) S – sub-mucosa; T – mucosa.

(d) Blood vessels/capillaries – transport products of digestion.
Lymph vessels – transport lipids.
Nerves – co-ordinate muscular contractions.
Glands – secrete enzymes/acids or alkalis/mucus.

4 (a)(i) P: Herbivore; Q: Carnivore.

(ii) P: Incisors in lower jaw only, with horny pad for cutting/ interlocking molars for grinding/gap or diastema/enamel ridges continue to grow.

Q: Sharp incisors to grip and tear flesh from bone/large canines for seizing or killing prey/tearing flesh/carnassials for shearing flesh/crushing bones.

(iii) A short gut in the carnivore reflects the ease with which protein is digested compared with the herbivore which has a cellulose diet.

(b)(i) The cud is mixed with cellulose-digesting bacteria; cud can be regurgitated; allows water to be reabsorbed; presence of bacteria in rumen; some absorption, e.g. of fatty acids.

(ii) Carnivores catch prey only periodically and can use their stomach to store their catch until the next time they make a kill/diet is mainly protein and it is the stomach where protein is digested.

5 (a) A parasite is an organism that lives on or in another organism called the host; and obtains nourishment from the host and causes it a degree of harm.

(b)(i) Pig.

(ii) The pig becomes infected if it feeds in places contaminated by human faeces.

(iii) Eating undercooked infected pork.

(c)(i) Suckers/hooks.

(ii) A thick cuticle/body covering which produces inhibitory substances to prevent digestion by the host's enzymes; or which resists host's immune response.

(d) To overcome the problem of transfer to another host/ to increase the chance of some of the offspring reaching another host.

Knowledge check answers

Knowledge checks BY1

1. cell wall; β; glycosidic; 180; hydrogen; microfibrils.
2. glycerol; unsaturated; phosphate; membranes.
3. A: tertiary; B: secondary; C: primary; D: quaternary.
4. A: glycosidic; B: ester; C: peptide.
5. A: transport; B: cooling; C: photosynthesis; D: insulation.
6. 1: B; 2: A; 3: D; 4: C.
7. 1: B; 2: A; 3: C.
8. 1: B; 2: B, D; 3: B, C; 4: A, D.
9. biological; ionic; active site; complex.
10. kinetic; inactive; optimum; hydrogen; tertiary; substrate; denatured.
11. active site; substrate; increased; cyanide.
12. immobilised; blood sugar.
13. nucleotides; deoxyribose; double helix; hydrogen; thymine; uracil; ribose.
14. A: metaphase; B: anaphase; C: anaphase; D: prophase; E: telophase.

Knowledge checks BY2

15. 1: C; 2: B; 3: A.
16. Kingdom, phylum, class, order, family, genus.
17. 1: C; 2: B; 3: D; 4: A.
18. jointed legs; chitin; ecdysis.
19. 1: C; 2: D; 3: B; 4: A.
20. amoeba; diffusion; surface area; volume; circulatory; haemoglobin; lungs; gills.
21. counter-current; blood; increases; diffusion gradient; gill plate.
22. 1: C; 2: E; 3: D; 4: A; 5: B.
23. 1: D; 2: B; 3: C; 4: A.
24. 1: B; 2: C; 3: A; 4: D; 5: E.
25. sino-atrial node; atrio-ventricular node; bundle of His/Purkinje/Purkyne fibres; contract; pulmonary artery.
26. plasma; erythrocytes; oxygen; oxyhaemoglobin; leucocytes; granulocytes/phagocytes; agranulocytes/lymphocytes.
27. 1: D; 2: B; 3: A; 4: C.
28. root hair; water potential; symplast; Casparian strip.
29. transpiration; stomata; xerophytes; sunken; cuticle; hydrophytes.
30. sucrose; source; sink; sieve tubes.
31. meiosis; zygote; internal; water.
32. 1: B; 2: C; 3: D; 4: A.
33. salivary glands; (salivary) amylase; villi/crypt of Lieberkuhn; glucose; fructose.
34. microvilli; surface area; capillaries; lacteal/lymphatic system.
35. side to side; horny pad; diastema; carnassials.
36. human; pig; reproduction; hooks; cuticle; surface area.

Glossary

absorption The passage of digested food through the gut wall into the blood.

activation energy The energy required to bring about a chemical reaction; lowered by the presence of enzymes.

active site The specific portion of an enzyme into which the substrate fits by means of weak chemical bonds.

active transport The movement of a substance across a membrane against a concentration gradient. The process requires energy in the form of ATP.

adaptation A feature that increases the chance of survival of an organism in its environment.

adaptive radiation The emergence of numerous species from a common ancestor introduced into an environment.

adenosine triphosphate (ATP) An activated nucleotide found in all living cells that acts as an energy carrier.

aerobic respiration A process requiring free oxygen to release energy from glucose.

affinity One molecule having a chemical attraction to another.

alveoli Air sacs in lungs providing a large surface area.

analogous Structures having the same function but a different origin.

asexual reproduction A type of reproduction involving only one parent that produces genetically identical offspring.

atrio-ventricular node (AVN) An area of tissue in the septum of the heart through which a wave of electrical excitation is passed to the Purkyne tissue.

autotrophic nutrition Green plants make their own complex organic materials by the process of photosynthesis.

binomial A system based on giving each organism two names, the name of its genus followed by the name of its species.

biodiversity A measure of the number of different species living on the planet.

biosensor The association of a biomolecule such as an enzyme with a transducer which produces an electrical signal in response to substrate transformation.

Bohr effect A phenomenon whereby at higher partial pressures of carbon dioxide the oxygen dissociation curve shifts to the right.

capillarity The tendency of water to rise in narrow tubes.

cardiac cycle The sequence of events taking place during one heartbeat.

cardiac muscle Type of muscle only found in the heart.

carnivore An animal which feeds on other animals.

Casparian strip A distinctive band of suberin around the endodermal cells of a plant root that prevents water passing via the cell walls into the xylem.

cell cycle A sequence of events that takes place from one cell division until the next.

chlorophyll The green pigment located within the chloroplasts of plants.

Chordata Animals possessing a vertebral column or backbone; also called vertebrates.

chromosome A threadlike, gene-carrying structure found in the nucleus.

chrysalis (pupa) A stage whereby the larva undergoes a period of change before emerging as an adult.

clone A group of genetically identical organisms formed from a single parent as a result of asexual reproduction.

cohesion The attraction between molecules of the same type.

competitive inhibitor A chemical that reduces the rate of activity of an enzyme by having a molecular shape similar to that of the substrate, competing with it for the active site of an enzyme.

condensation reaction Chemical process in which two molecules combine to form a more complex molecule with the elimination of water.

conservation The management of habitats to maintain or restore species diversity and ecosystem function.

convergent evolution The tendency of unrelated organisms to acquire similar structures.

counter-current flow The mechanism by which the efficiency of exchange between two substances is increased by having them flowing in opposite directions e.g. blood in the gills of a fish flows in the opposite direction in which water passes over the gills, maximising oxygen uptake and carbon dioxide loss.

crossing over The reciprocal exchange of genetic material between non-sister chromatids during synapsis of meiosis I.

cuticle Exposed, non-cellular outer layer of certain animals, e.g. insects, and the leaves of plants. Waxy and impermeable, reduces water loss.

cytoplasm The entire contents of the cell, excluding the nucleus, and bounded by the plasma membrane.

deciduous Plants that shed all their leaves together at one season.

decomposer Organisms, fungi and bacteria that break down dead organic matter to obtain nutrients.

denaturation The permanent damage to the structure and shape of a protein, e.g. enzymes, due to changes in factors such as temperature and pH.

differentiation The process by which cells become specialised for different functions.

diffusion The passive movement of a substance down a concentration gradient from a region of high concentration to a region of low concentration.

digestion The breakdown of large insoluble food molecules into smaller soluble molecules by means of enzymes.

diploid (cell) A cell containing two sets of chromosomes ($2n$), one set inherited from each parent.

double circulation A circulatory system in which the blood travels twice through the heart in one complete circuit of the body.

ecosystem A level of ecological study that includes all the organisms in a given area as well as the abiotic factors with which they interact.

endangered species A species that is in danger of extinction throughout all or a significant portion of its range.

endocytosis The engulfing of material by the plasma membrane bringing it into the cell inside a vesicle.

endodermis A ring of cells surrounding the xylem tissue having an impermeable waterproof barrier through their cell walls.

enzyme A protein that acts as a catalyst, altering the rate of a chemical reaction without being used up by the reaction.

ester bond A bond formed between glycerol and fatty acids.

eukaryotic cell A cell with a membrane-bound nucleus and membrane-bound organelles.

evolution The process by which new species are formed from pre-existing ones over very long periods of time.

exocytosis The release of substances contained in a vesicle from a cell through the cytoplasm.

exoskeleton An outer body covering made of chitin in Arthropods.

extinction The process by which a species ceases to exist on Earth, e.g. due to a failure to adapt successfully to a changing environment.

facilitated diffusion Diffusion involving the presence of protein carrier molecules to allow the passive movement of substances across plasma membranes.

fertilisation The fusion of male and female gametes to produce a diploid zygote.

flaccid A condition where no more water can leave the cell and the cell is said to be plasmolysed.

gamete A sex cell containing half the number of chromosomes (haploid) as body cells.

gaseous exchange The movement of gases between an organism and its environment.

gene A length of DNA on a chromosome which codes for a particular polypeptide.

glycosidic bond The link between monosaccharide units.

haemoglobin Globular protein in blood that has a high affinity for oxygen which it transports around the body as oxy-haemoglobin.

haploid Cells that contain only a single copy of each chromosome, e.g. gametes.

herbivore An animal that feeds only on plant material.

heterotrophic Organisms that consume ready-made food.

hierarchical A classification system based on ranking groups in ascending order from large groups to small groups.

homologous chromosomes A pair of chromosomes that possess genes for the same characters at corresponding loci and therefore determine the same features. One homologous chromosome is inherited from the father, the other from the mother.

hydrolysis The breaking down of large molecules into smaller molecules by the addition of water.

hydrophyte A plant adapted to growing submerged or partly submerged in water.

hydrostatic The pressure exerted by a fluid.

immobilised enzyme Enzyme that is fixed, bound or trapped on an inert matrix such as alginate beads.

induced fit The change in shape of the active site of an enzyme so that it binds more snugly to the substrate, induced by the entry of the substrate.

intrinsic proteins Proteins of the cell surface membrane that completely span the phospholipid bilayer from one side to the other.

isomers Compounds that have the same chemical formula but which differ in the arrangement of the atoms.

isotonic solutions Solutions of equal solute concentration.

kinetic energy Energy possessed by an object due to its motion.

larva The young or immature form of an insect.

lignin A complex compound which impregnates the cellulose matrix of plant cell walls, making the wall strong and rigid and impervious to gases, water and solutes.

lymph A colourless fluid, derived from tissue fluid, found in the lymphatic system of vertebrates.

lymphocyte A type of white blood cell involved in the immune response.

meiosis A two-stage type of cell division in sexually reproducing organisms that results in gametes with half the chromosome number of the original cell.

mesophyte Plant which flourishes in habitats with adequate water supply, typical of temperate regions.

metabolism All the organism's chemical processes, consisting of anabolic and catabolic pathways.

metamorphosis A stage in the life cycle of certain animals involving a period of change from the larval stage to the adult.

microfibril Bundles of cellulose chains packed together.

mitosis A type of cell division in which the daughter cells have the same number of chromosomes as the parent cell.

myogenic The contraction of heart muscle initiated from within the heart itself and not due to nervous stimulation.

myoglobin An oxygen-binding molecule found in muscle which acts as an oxygen store.

niche An organism's role in an ecosystem.

non-competitive inhibitor A chemical that reduces the rate of activity of an enzyme by binding at a position other than the active site altering the overall shape of the enzyme.

nucleotide A complex chemical made up of an organic base, a sugar and a phosphate.

nucleus The chromosome-containing organelle of a eukaryotic cell.

operculum A covering over the gills in bony fish.

organelle A functionally and structurally distinct part of a cell.

osmosis The net movement of water molecules across a selectively permeable membrane from a region of high water potential to a region of lower water potential.

parasite An organism that obtains nutrients from another living organism, known as the host, causing it a degree of harm and often death.

pentadactyl Having five digits.

pentose sugar Possessing five carbon atoms e.g. ribose.

peptide bond The chemical bond formed between two amino acids following condensation.

peristalsis Rhythmic wave of muscular contractions in the gut.

phagocytosis Mechanism by which cells transport large particles across the plasma membrane into the cell.

phloem tissue Tissue containing sieve tubes and companion cells responsible for the translocation of sucrose and amino acids from the leaves to the rest of the plant.

photosynthesis The process in green plants by which carbon dioxide and water combine, using light energy, to form glucose and water.

phylogeny The evolutionary relationship between organisms.

plankton Microscopic organisms that occur near the surface of oceans, ponds and lakes.

plasmodesmata Fine strands of cytoplasm that extend through pores in adjacent plant cell walls connecting the cytoplasm of one cell with another.

plasmolysis The withdrawal of the cytoplasm and the plasma membrane from the cell wall when a cell loses water by osmosis.

polymer Long chain of repeating monomer units.

potometer A device which indirectly measures the rate of water loss during transpiration by measuring the rate of water uptake.

respiratory surface The site of gaseous exchange, e.g. gills, lungs.

root pressure The force created at the base of the xylem vessel by the influx of water along a water potential gradient.

ruminant A herbivore possessing a stomach or rumen divided into four chambers.

saprobiont (saprophyte) Organism that feeds on dead, decaying matter.

selective permeability A property of biological membranes which allows some substances to cross.

sexual reproduction Reproduction involving two parents, each of which provides a gamete which fuse during fertilisation, resulting in offspring that have unique combinations of genes.

sino-atrial node (SAN) An area of the heart muscle in the right atrium that controls and co-ordinates the contraction of the heart. Also known as the pacemaker.

sister chromatids Replicated forms of a chromosome joined together by the centromere and eventually separated during cell division.

solute A substance that is dissolved in a solvent. Solutes and solvents form a solution.

species A group of similar organisms capable of interbreeding to produce fertile offspring.

species diversity The number and relative abundance of species in a community.

stoma (pl. stomata) A pore surrounded by two guard cells, through which gases diffuse in and out of the leaf.

symbiosis The association between two members of different species where both organisms derive benefit from the relationship.

systole A stage in the cardiac cycle in which the heart muscle contracts.

taxonomy The branch of biology concerned with naming and classifying the various forms of life.

tissue fluid (intercellular fluid) Fluid filling the spaces between cells; plasma minus proteins seeps from capillaries and bathes the cells.

translocation The transport of sugars and other substances through phloem cells in plants.

transpiration The evaporation of water from leaves, resulting in the movement of water up through the xylem vessels (the transpiration stream).

turgid A condition in the cell where no more water can enter. Additional entry of water is prevented by the cell wall stopping further expansion of the cell.

variation The differences in characteristics of members of the same species.

ventilation A mechanism enabling air to be transferred from the atmosphere to the respiratory surface.

water potential The tendency of a solution to gain or lose water; water moves from a solution with high water potential (less negative) to one with a low water potential (more negative). Water potential is decreased by the addition of solute and increased by the application of pressure. Pure water has a water potential of zero.

xerophyte A plant adapted to survive in conditions where water is in short supply.

xylem vessel A dead, empty vessel with lignified walls and no end walls, through which water is transported in the plant.

zygote The diploid product of the fusion of haploid gametes in sexual reproduction.

Index

apsis 63

em, definition of 31

ble 102

phage 32

worm 132, 139–140

onomy 72–73, 78

mperature 38, 47, 49, 50, 52, 114

lakoids 29

ymine 58

tissue 29, 30, 31, 63, 85, 87, 90, 92, 93, 99,
100, 101, 103, 104, 105, 106, 107, 108,
111–112, 113, 116, 117, 118, 119, 128, 131,
132, 133, 137, 140

tissue fluid 108

tonoplast 26, 30

trachea 84, 90

tracheae 77, 85, 89, 99

tracheid 110

transducer 53

translocation 117–119

transpiration 111, 112–114, 115, 116

transport system 26, 98–100

triglyceride 14, 15

triose sugar 10

turgid 30, 40, 41, 94, 115

U

ultrastructure 25, 26, 27

unicellular 25, 74, 84

uracil 59

urea 98, 137

V

vacuole 26, 28, 30, 40, 41, 75, 111

valve 87, 89, 99, 101, 102, 103

variation (genetic) 63, 64

vascular bundle 110

vein 90, 91, 99, 100–101, 102, 103, 108

ventilation 85, 86, 87, 88, 91

ventricle 101, 102, 103–104

vertebral column 76, 78

vesicle 26, 28, 29, 30, 42

villus (pl. villi) 135, 136

virus 32, 139

W

water

potential (WP) 40–41, 94, 108, 111, 112,
113, 114, 115, 116, 118, 119

properties of 20

uptake 114–115

vapour 113–114, 116

white blood cell (WBC) 28, 42, 104

X

xerophyte 115–116

xylem 31, 109, 110, 111–113, 116, 118, 119,
128

Z

zygote 63, 126, 127

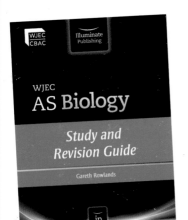
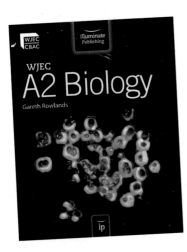
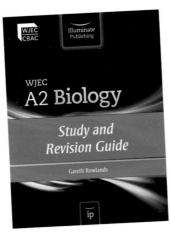